D1373274

MINDFULNESS
The New Science of Health and Happiness

contents

Parts of this edition appeared previously in TIME, Health *and* Real Simple.

BEING HERE

Just because you're busy and distracted, that doesn't mean you have to miss out on life

By Lisa Lombardi

WE HAVE ALL HAD THOSE MOments of: I'm here, but I'm not here.

Mine came while I was in the bleachers at my then-7-year-old's baseball game. "Mom," my son called out from the field, "look up from your phone. I don't want you to get hit with the ball!"

The other parents around me laughed—because I was busted, and also because who couldn't relate?

We live in a time when we can be present in so many moments, almost as they happen, across the globe. Watch a college roommate reach the summit of Mount Rainier in real time. Skype with the kids from a business trip in Asia. See a streaming video of your newborn niece wriggle 30 seconds after she comes out into the world. We have access to those astonishing moments, and we wouldn't have it any other way. But what about the moments unfolding right in front of us? The ordinary ones. That Little League game. The last out and the nice hustle off the field, the sound of the players' rhyming chants and the warmth from having parked yourself in the last patch of afternoon sunlight.

Being mindful in the real world isn't always easy, but if we get even a little better at it, we benefit in crucial ways. A growing body of research attests to the profound mind-body benefits of getting centered. Mindfulness techniques, including meditation and deep, rhythmic breathing (see pages 23 and 44) are some of the best lifestyle tools we have to control stress (page 16), improve sleep (page 24) and even avoid illness (page 30).

Clearing your mind can also lead to deeper thinking, reveals a new study published in *Psychological Science*. Researchers Moshe Bar and Shira Baror set up experiments in which people were given a collection of numbers to remember and then asked to free-associate words. Some groups were asked to remember fewer numbers than the other groups. The people who had more numbers in their head consistently gave the least creative, most statistically common replies (such as "white"/"black"), while the ones with

4

fewer numbers weighing down their brain consistently gave the more imaginative responses ("white"/"cloud") and responded in less time. The likely explanation: having a cluttered brain gets in the way of deep and agile thinking.

"Mental load, such as to-do lists, is a part of life, and we have to accept it, but we should be aware of its influences on our subjective experience," explains Bar, a neuroscientist and the director of the Multidisciplinary Brain Research Center at Bar-Ilan University in Israel. "Any such load consumes some of our mental resources, thereby diminishing what we can allocate to the experience before us. A clearer mind affords a fuller experience."

Stress and ruminations "tax our ability to be creative as well as to really immerse ourselves

If we get even a little better at being mindful, we benefit in crucial ways.

in experiences," adds Bar, who is also a professor at Harvard Medical School. Why? Our brain normally switches between exploratory and exploitatory modes. In exploratory mode we're open to new experiences and have a desire to learn, even if there's risk involved. This is how many of us operate on trips to new places. In exploitatory function, on the other hand, we tend to rely on existing knowledge and lean toward predictable situations. "When our mental capacity is loaded, we are more exploitatory and less creative," Bar says.

The solution, as with so many things, is stress reduction. Meditation, yoga and aerobic exercise can help you achieve, as Bar puts it, "relatively rapid calmness of mind," so every day feels a little more like an adventure—and not because you just got hit in the head with a ball.

PART ONE

Outsmart Stress

WHY EVERY MIND NEEDS MINDFULNESS

More and more of us are looking for peace in our crazy-busy days—and discovering that being present is its own reward

By Mary Elizabeth Williams

AM BRINGING MY AWARENESS outward. I am perceiving the dense humidity of a summer afternoon as I stand on a city sidewalk and the way the hot air feels inside my lungs. I am present to observe the passage of time and how it seems somehow slowed down. I am cognizant of sharing this space with a small cluster of men and women around me. Or to put it another way, the meditation teacher has stood up the class. Some days, the lessons in mindfulness take you in unexpected directions.

Ask 10 people to define "mindfulness," and you'll likely get 10 different responses. But the basic concept of the word is straightforward. It's about putting down our juggling balls for a little bit. It's about embracing the beauty of monotasking. It's about, as mindfulness author and instructor Jon Kabat-Zinn has put it, "paying attention in a particular way: on purpose, in the present moment and nonjudgmentally."

Though the contemplative practice has its roots in several of the world's major belief systems—most recognizably Buddhism but also in Hinduism, Judaism and Christianity—you don't have to subscribe to any particular religion or philosophy to experience mindfulness. And if lately you've felt that some psychic decluttering might be just what the doctor ordered, you're far from alone.

It's no coincidence that as we find ourselves increasingly barraged with distractions—a 2013 University of Southern California study estimated that the average American consumes an astonishing 13-plus hours of media a day—we simultaneously find ourselves in the midst of a mindfulness revolution. You can see evidence everywhere. Hospitals across the country are increasingly using meditation, yoga, guided imagery and similar alternative practices as part of the health-care offerings to patients undergoing surgery, pain management, cancer treat-

> # Mindfulness is about putting down our juggling balls for a little bit. It's about embracing the beauty of monotasking.

ment and more. Corporations such as American Express and Nike have been jumping on the bandwagon, taking mindfulness training programs to their staff. Apps like Headspace—"a gym membership for your mind"—have been downloaded millions of times. A 2012 study by the National Institutes of Health found that more than 33% of Americans said they had used alternative health practices, including meditation, over the course of the year.

I am a longtime, if erratic and extraordinarily imperfect, practitioner of meditation. But recently, as the demands of 21st-century life—work, parenting, a seemingly limitless and often self-imposed deluge of emails to answer and texts to reply to and Instagram posts to Like—have ramped up, I've found myself embracing one of the greatest side effects of my practice: the mindfulness that helps calm me wherever and whenever, even in the midst of my most cacophonous moments. And like a growing population of individuals similarly chafing against the rigors of what the writer Linda Stone has aptly diagnosed as "continuous partial attention," I've experienced the proven physical and mental benefits of regular pauses.

HEALTH BENEFITS

The perks of mindfulness are tangible. The American Psychological Association cites it as a hopeful strategy for alleviating depression, anxiety and pain. But mindfulness doesn't just seem to boost mood and perception—the effects go deeper. Mindfulness practice can shrink the brain's jumpy "fight or flight" center, the amygdala, according to 2013 research out of the University of Pittsburgh and Carnegie Mellon University. Another study, done at the University of Wisconsin–Madison, found that people who meditate regularly have different patterns of brain electricity, potentially leading to more efficient attention-paying and learning. Change your thoughts, and

Participants attend an evening session at MNDFL, a meditation studio that opened in New York in 2016.

maybe you can even change your brain.

For me, mindfulness has been a powerful tool against my migraines and panic attacks. It's a masterful hack, using my own thoughts to quell my stormy brain, reducing my migraine-medication consumption and my shrink visits. But that doesn't mean I don't still often struggle, like everybody else, through the current of information overload.

"I think there's been a kind of confusion in our culture where people have felt that they have to be anxious, uptight and always on

the go to be effective," says psychologist and author Daniel Goleman, whose groundbreaking best sellers include *Emotional Intelligence* and *The Meditative Mind*. Goleman notes that in our competitively frantic culture, "people are feeling a little desperation. It used to be you left work and went home. Now you've got your devices that follow you everywhere. The body is designed to be energetic and active and then recover. People don't have any recovery time—there's been this silent, invisible ratcheting up of invasion of our space." The

Former Google engineer Chade-Meng Tan, author of the book *Search Inside Yourself*, initiated mindfulness training at the company.

result, he says, is that "everyone's multitasking like crazy—and the more you do it, the worse you get at it."

IN PRAISE OF MONOTASKING

It might sound counterintuitive, but it's true. Research out of the University of California, Irvine, reveals that not only do people tend to switch activities an alarming every three minutes during the course of a typical workday, but it takes them significantly longer to get back on the original task. And as U.C. Irvine professor Gloria Mark told *Fast Company* in 2008, all that ricocheting leads to "higher levels of stress, frustration, mental effort, feeling of time pressure and mental workload."

In contrast, Goleman says, "a relaxed, alert state is the optimum for any performance in any field. Athletes try to get in that state, because that's when the brain processes best and the mind functions at its peak."

No wonder mindfulness is increasingly being integrated into the workplace, with initiatives such as Google's nine-year-old Search Inside Yourself training program. Since 2007 it has been used by big-name businesses in the tech world and beyond, deploying centuries-old techniques to boost productivity and stave off burnout.

Yet many of us, myself included, persistently wear our overstimulation as a badge of honor. When was the last time you answered a job listing for a position in a thoughtfully paced environment, for a candidate able to handle one thing at a time?

But if you're the kind of person whose immediate reaction to meditation is an insistence that your brain just works too fast and you simply can't, you're exactly the kind of person who needs it most. Author and meditation teacher Sharon Salzberg says, "I hear people say, 'I tried it once; I failed at it.' I think the fear and the sense of having failed are born of some misconception of what is supposed to happen. Most of us have a pretty

> **Many of us, myself included, persistently wear our overstimulation as a badge of honor.**

bad habit of being unjust with ourselves. But if we sat down at the piano for the first time and couldn't play an exquisite piece of music, we wouldn't give up."

It also helps to understand that there are no prizes handed out for attaining the World's Greatest Mindfulness. Salzberg instead advises to think of mindfulness as "about connecting to our experience in a different way—a quality of awareness where we're not adding stuff." Call it the life-changing magic of tidying up your own thoughts. She adds, "For many of us, we start wondering what's it going to feel like next week, next month. When you see that anticipation rising, you can come back to the now. Mindfulness helps us wake up."

That's how my friend Whitney, a digital editor at a high-profile media company, learned to let go and found her flow. Living in New York shortly after 9/11, she was experiencing a variety of stress-related health issues when a friend persuaded her to attend a meditation class. It was not exactly a duck-to-water experience.

"I'm incredibly speedy; I'm incredibly distracted," she says. "I remember the first time I sat in meditation, I was just thrilled that I could sit still for a half-hour. There are some people who are immediately like, 'Yup, got it,' but it was so not the case for me." Instead, she admits, "I honestly think for the first few years I just kinda sat there." She adds, "Meditation is an amazing practice, but what matters is what happens off the cushion. It's the application and how you work with mindfulness in your life. It means I'm trying to stay in the present in the way that I approach my work or the way I'm washing a dish. I'm trying to pay more attention."

Richard Davidson, the founder of the Center for Healthy Minds at the University of Wisconsin–Madison, has built his career on studying just these issues. Consistent practice, he says, can improve your skill set to "accept things without strongly attaching to them"—a major stress-busting technique.

"It's not that we don't experience intense emotions," he says. "It's that they will recover to baseline more quickly. We may experience emotion that's appropriate in the situation but then not have it bleed over into the next. There's no lingering, no stickiness."

Over time, I have come to look upon my practice as I do my local pizzeria and my weekend naps: not always great, but usually plenty good enough for my spirit. Mindfulness for me has meant purging a slew of apps from my phone and my notifications from almost everything. It's meant overcoming my dread of boredom and sometimes going out for a run without listening to music. It's meant similarly giving myself permission to not eat lunch in front of my computer. It's been taking a moment to sniff a tomato before chopping it for a salad or to take a few slow, steadying breaths when I'm feeling overwhelmed. These are not exactly revolutionary practices. They are challenging. I often blow it. That's kind of the point.

MAKING THE COMMITMENT

I am sitting on a cushion in New York's tranquil and spacious MNDFL studio. My eyes are closed and my breath is steady. I am listening to our instructor guide us through a compassion-awakening meditation. I am in the zone. Then I remember I need to stop on the way home for milk and bananas. But that's not a failure of my meditation—that's an example of mindfulness. I recognize that I've tuned out, and I try again. "If you drift off, you're just getting to know what's going on in your mind," MNDFL co-founder Lodro Rinzler later affirms to me. Mindfulness, he says, is "something that's hard to mess up."

As if to prove the point, when class is over and I'm standing at the supermarket line, I am doing something remarkable. I'm not looking at my phone. I'm not listening to a podcast in one ear while listening to the grocery Muzak in the other. I'm just . . . buying food. It feels

surprisingly civilized. As Goleman puts it, "Every time you do a rep with a free weight, you're strengthening a muscle. Every time you bring your mind back, the stronger it gets, the more focused."

If there's any downside to mindfulness, though, it's that lately, I can't help feeling inundated by, well, mindfulness. The word appears on popular adult coloring books and vegan mayonnaise labels. At times, mindfulness seems like this year's kale—a hipster buzzword on the brink of wearing out its welcome.

But authentic self-care is not about sandwich spreads, and it definitely shouldn't be dismissed for being trendy. Rinzler points out, "Back in the '50s, if you said you were going for a run, someone would ask, 'Who's chasing you?' I think this is the next wave of that. I think we're hitting this point with mindfulness—all these studies have come out that show you're going to sleep better; you're going to be less reactive. Now it's your doctors and not just your hippie friends talking about it." Like engaging in physical exercise or eating a more balanced, plant-based diet, consistency matters more than all-or-nothing, built-to-fail extremes. And like all of those things, a dedication to mindfulness is a lifelong project.

I am a work in progress. If you happen to pass me sometime on the street, you will note that I will not be floating serenely above the sidewalk as light pours out of my third eye. You will instead see a busy mom, most likely hustling her kids to the next thing they need to be hustled to, tapping on her phone in reply to some new urgent demand from somebody, gamely trying to navigate the throng like a character in an '80s-era arcade game. But I'm trying to pay as much attention as I can, as often as I can. I keep trying because it keeps being worth it, because, as the philosopher Simone Weil observed, decades before the digital age, "Attention is the rarest and purest form of generosity." And it's the gift worth giving ourselves.

> **Consistency in mindfulness matters more than all-or-nothing, built-to-fail extremes. It's a lifelong project.**

Eight Ways to Be Zen at Work

This is how you can improve well-being on the job

BY MANDY OAKLANDER

TALLYING UP SICK DAYS ISN'T THE ONLY WAY TO TELL HOW SOMEONE AT WORK IS FARING. A recent analysis of American workers found that despite the rise of corporate wellness programs, disengagement at the office costs the U.S. $550 billion each year, and work-related stress tacks on an additional $300 billion. But new studies are turning up surprising strategies that improve both well-being and productivity. For starters, people are happier and more engaged when they accept that work is the pits sometimes, a recent study suggests. Another idea: find ways to detach. "If your goal is feeling better, you need to get your head out of work," says Reb Rebele, a researcher with Wharton People Analytics at the University of Pennsylvania. Experts recommend these evidence-based tricks for reducing stress on the job. (And don't worry: "Learn to meditate at your desk" isn't on the list.)

Do someone a five-minute favor

Volunteering helps people connect to others, which aids in recovering from stress. You can do the same thing at work by, say, getting a cup of coffee for someone who's having a bad day. Spot a need, and, for five minutes, be the one to fill it.

Play with a puppy

Beg your boss, if necessary: one study showed that when employees brought their dogs to work, they felt less stressed and were just as productive as they were on canine-free days.

Hide your phone

Even if you're not using it, simply being able to see a cellphone hinders your ability to focus on tough tasks, a pair of 2014 studies found. The mere presence of a phone also made people trust and like each other less than if it weren't present, according to other research.

Take a break before lunch

People who take breaks in the morning feel more restored and less emotionally exhausted than people who take breaks in the afternoon, a 2016 study found. Morning breakers were more likely to say they were satisfied with their jobs, too.

Let yourself procrastinate

In one study, a researcher gave people a task and let some of them play five minutes of Minesweeper. Those who played the game generated ideas considerably more creative than those who got right to the task. Their minds were most likely chewing away at the problem in the background.

Disappear for a bit

Take a 10-minute walk daily—it helps to put it on your calendar—and don't ruminate about work while you're gone, Rebele advises. Instead, listen to a podcast, make a phone call, do a walking meditation or bring a friend to talk about something non-work-related [see right].

Gossip with your co-workers

"Social time is really valuable, even for introverts," Rebele says. But to truly detach—and reap the productivity and wellness benefits of a solid break—you have to keep the conversation office-free.

End the day like you mean it

A 2016 study found that if people think they should be reachable after work, they feel less in control and have more of the stress hormone cortisol. Meanwhile, another study shows that as long as your work gets done, putting in more hours doesn't make you a better worker in your boss's eyes.

Sources: Global Wellness Institute; *Journal of Occupational Health Psychology*; *Social Psychology*; *International Journal of Workplace Health Management*; *Journal of Applied Psychology*; *Originals*, by Adam Grant; *Harvard Business Review*

SAVE YOURSELF FROM STRESS

Before tension wreaks havoc on your body,
learn how to keep calm and motor on

By Jancee Dunn

THERE'S A CERTAIN SORT OF person mind-body expert Alice Domar sees all too often: the type with a high-octane life who has no idea that her stress levels are sabotaging her health. "One woman had two kids and worked 80 hours a week," recalls Domar, who is the executive director of the Domar Center for Mind/Body Health in Waltham, Mass. "She came to me because she was thinking of trying for a third child and was concerned about her irregular periods—but when I took a complete history, I found out that she had a host of physical symptoms, including frequent headaches and insomnia. It never occurred to her that they had anything to do with her intense lifestyle."

That's the insidious thing about stress: it infiltrates our bodies even as our heads are spinning. And it's ever-present; the American Psychological Association reports that 34% of Americans say their stress levels have shot up in the past year. Left untreated, stress can lead to serious ills, including heart disease, depression, anxiety and diabetes. It could even speed up the spread of breast and ovarian cancers, research suggests. Untamed tension may also pop up as aches and ills that make us feel crummy on a daily basis.

As annoying as those eye twitches and stomach knots are, we should be thanking our bodies for the heads-up, doctors say. "Physical symptoms that accompany stress are part of the body's warning system," notes Darshan Mehta, the medical director of Massachusetts General Hospital's Benson-Henry Institute for Mind Body Medicine in Boston. They nudge you to take better care of yourself. Ahead, everything you've ever wondered about how stress affects your system but were too frazzled to ask.

Why does stress have a physical effect if it's a mental thing?

Forget your tyrant boss; blame the woolly rhinoceros. "Stress activates a psychophysiologic response—the mind perceives a threat or emergency, and your body reacts," according to Michael McKee, who was a psycholo-

gist at the Cleveland Clinic. You're probably familiar with the fight-or-flight effect: your system churns out the stress chemicals adrenaline, norepinephrine and cortisol, causing your heart to race and blood pressure to increase as oxygen goes to your large muscles. In the Stone Age, this response would save us from danger. Today it basically causes our brain to overreact, interpreting mildly stressful situations (like planning a holiday dinner for 25 people) as run-for-the-hills emergencies. Over time, constantly cycling into a revved-up state can cause wear and tear on the heart, muscles and brain.

In 2012, researchers from Carnegie Mellon University discovered why frequently having high levels of cortisol can do damage. Cortisol helps turn off inflammation in the body, but prolonged stress makes immune cells insensitive to the hormone's regulatory effect. As a result, the inflammatory response that the immune system normally launches to protect the body goes into overdrive. That excess inflammation may lead to anything from the common cold to, in the long run, heart attacks, stroke and autoimmune disorders. A 2014 study revealed that people under significant pressure at work had a 45% higher risk of Type 2 diabetes.

Do events such as a death or divorce affect you more than everyday hassles?

Both acute stress and the daily kind can do harm, weakening your immunity and triggering flare-ups of migraines, irritable bowel syndrome and arthritis. "Chronic activation of your stress response can contribute to disease," Mehta says. One study from Pennsylvania State University discovered that people who got distressed by little annoyances were more likely to have chronic health conditions such as arthritis-induced pain 10 years later.

A key aid to weathering life's drama: friends. Research shows that when faced with a big upset, many of us cope by leaning on social supports, which dramatically reduces stress and strengthens resilience. Thing is, little hassles have a way of getting under your

This Is Your Body on Stress

BRAIN
A steady flow of cortisol from chronic stress can damage your short-term memory; stress can actually reduce gray matter.

MOUTH
Stress hormones mobilize energy to muscles; at night, some people may release it by grinding their teeth (a.k.a. bruxism), causing jaw pain and headaches.

NOSE
Persistent tension can cause seasonal allergy flare-ups, per a recent study, possibly because it prompts a negative immune response.

HEART
During moments of high anxiety, stress hormones narrow the arteries in the heart and increase heart rate, which over time may raise your risk of developing cardiovascular disease.

FERTILITY
Stress can alter signals to the hypothalamus, the part of the brain that regulates hormones that trigger ovaries to release eggs each month. High levels of stress hormones also affect the body's main reproductive hormone, GnRH.

STOMACH
Stress slows the GI tract's movement and digestive process while upping the chances of inflammation (which can lead to pain, gas or diarrhea). Research shows that stress can even change the balance of gut bacteria, weakening the immune system.

BACK
Adrenaline from the sympathetic nervous system alerts muscles to tense up in preparation for action. Pain and spasms in your neck and back may result, especially if they're weak spots for you.

WAISTLINE
Anxiety can hurt your metabolism, suggests a new study. Women who experienced one or more stressful events during the previous 24 hours burned 104 fewer calories in the seven hours after eating a high-fat meal than those who stayed stress-free.

skin—you're not receiving support for the irritation you feel about a long grocery-store line (except maybe from your mother).

Tension makes my lower back ache. My husband gets headaches. Why is that?

Everyone has his or her weak health spot. Think about it: maybe you always get chest colds, say, while your spouse sails through winter with just the sniffles. "Stress impacts all your systems—musculoskeletal, cardiovascular, gastrointestinal, respiratory, everything," McKee said. "But some systems are stronger than others, and stress produces the worst symptoms in the most vulnerable ones."

Why do some people wig out more than others?

It's nature and nurture. We model our parents' reactions to stress, experts say, and also have a genetic predisposition to be reactive or calm. One study commissioned by the National Institutes of Health found that we inherit varying amounts of neuropeptide Y, an anxiety-reducing compound released during stress.

Can it affect how you age?

Yes. (Sorry.) Stress has been shown to affect aging at the cellular level. The journal *PLOS One* recently published two studies showing that stress may mess with telomeres, the caps on the ends of our chromosomes that protect

Position Yourself Calm

Three ways to keep your body more relaxed—and less prone to tightening up from anxiety

AT YOUR COMPUTER

The ideal posture, per Gerard Girasole and Cara Hartman, the co-authors of *The 7-Minute Back Pain Solution*: knees should be even with hips (if not, use a footstool), with your computer monitor at eye level. And don't cradle your phone between your shoulder and ear, which strains the neck.

WHEN YOU'RE DRIVING

To minimize upper-back strain, hold the wheel in the "3 and 9" position. Traffic at a standstill? Says Kristin McGee, a yoga and Pilates instructor in New York: Turn to your right, reaching your left arm for the passenger seat. Inhale and exhale deeply for two breaths before twisting to the other side.

WHILE YOU SLEEP

"Sleeping on your stomach or curled into a ball can tense up your back, neck or spine," cautions Deborah Carr, the author of *Worried Sick: How Stress Hurts Us and How to Bounce Back*. Train yourself to sleep on your back; after a couple of weeks, it should feel more natural.

Five Habits That Bring Serenity Now

1. TAKE THE SCENIC ROUTE

Any bit of exercise is a stress reducer, but strolling in nature is ideal. One Japanese study found a link between chemicals released by trees, called phytoncides, and lowered levels of stress hormones.

2. GET MORE MAGNESIUM

This vital mineral is depleted quickly when you're under duress—and it's a vicious cycle, because without enough, you feel more emotional and reactive, says New York nutritionist Dana James. Eat more dark, leafy greens (think spinach and kale). Or down a smoothie made with magnesium-rich bananas, cocoa and almond milk.

3. PULL EARS, FEEL BETTER

A trick to try from Steve Kravitz, a Nashville, Tenn., physical therapist: "Hold your ears midway down with two fingers, in line with your ear canal. Gently pull both at a 45-degree angle away from your head and hold for 60 seconds. This calms the nerves that surround the central nervous system."

4. TURN OFF THE PINGING

A British study of office workers found that when they read and sent email, their heart rate, blood pressure and cortisol level spiked. Before you check Gmail again, ask yourself, Can it wait? (Yes, it can.)

5. HAVE A HAPPY CRY

Here is justification for watching heartwarming pet videos on YouTube: chemicals that build up during stress may be released through tears.

DNA as it replicates. Telomeres (like most of us) get shorter with age—and, as it turns out, with high levels of stress. As telomeres dwindle, genetic material can be damaged, leading to cell death. Meanwhile, researchers suspect that high cortisol levels from chronic stress break down the proteins collagen and elastin, which are responsible for skin elasticity—bringing us one step closer to looking like Abe Lincoln after the Civil War.

Of course we all need to manage stress. But if you aren't about to join a monastery, how do you deal?

Exercise is all-important, and not just for the endorphin rush: a mere 42 minutes of vigorous activity over a three-day period can reduce the impact of stress on telomere length, say scientists at the University of California, San Francisco. A balanced diet and adequate sleep are also essential, so go easy on the brownies and late-night binges of *Orange Is the New Black*. Getting lost in a hobby is another proven tension tamer—so when you're playing Candy Crush or shopping for shoes, you can indignantly tell your family that you're doing it for your health.

Mind-body techniques are especially beneficial. A 2014 Carnegie Mellon study found that just three 25-minute sessions of meditation can alleviate stress. Tai chi is receiving a lot of health buzz—one recent review of 40 studies published in the journal *BMC Complementary and Alternative Medicine* pointed to its stress-lowering properties. Sometimes described as meditation in motion, it calms nerves with deep breathing and improves flexibility.

In the end, nothing will help your stressed-out self if you ignore your symptoms. "The one point I make to patients all the time is that the body and brain are not subtle about telling you when you're stressed," Domar says. "When you get regular headaches or you're not sleeping well, stop and think to yourself, What's going on? Don't just pop pills and plow ahead."

Breathing Lessons

Wait, don't exhale just yet! By learning how to slow your breath, you can dial down your whole stress response

BY MANDY OAKLANDER

RESEARCH IS MOUNTING THAT A NATUral, potent source of stress relief is right in front of your nose. New science is showing that slowing down and deepening your breathing can have profound effects on well-being. "Many researchers can't imagine how something so simple could actually have effects on physiology," says Andrew Weil, a physician and the founder of the Arizona Center for Integrative Medicine at the University of Arizona. Breathing exercises—a staple of mindfulness and yoga practices—have been shown to help control blood pressure, improve heart rate, make arteries more flexible and activate the parasympathetic nervous system, which tamps down the body's fight-or-flight response to stress. Weil and other experts now believe deep breathing has a place in a clinical setting.

"It's enough to warrant applications in several areas of medicine," says Luciano Bernardi, an internal-medicine professor whose research shows that slow-breathing exercises improve exercise capacity in patients with chronic heart failure. "We've shown that this simple thing has a fantastic series of effects."

> "I think breath is the only function through which you can influence the involuntary nervous system."
> —DR. ANDREW WEIL

Sit in a position that is comfortable enough to sustain for a few minutes of alternate-nostril breathing. (Sitting in a chair is just fine.) This is one of many breathing exercises shown to have some health benefits [see right].

Make a "hang 10" sign with your right hand. Hold your right thumb over your right nostril to plug it closed. Inhale slowly through the left nostril until your lungs are full. Hold for four seconds.

Release the right nostril, and plug the left with your right pinkie. Slowly exhale. Once you've exhaled fully, inhale through the right nostril and then exhale through your left. Do about four rounds on each side—or more if you have time.

Sources: *Psychophysiology; Medical Science Monitor; Indian Journal of Physiology and Pharmacology; Journal of Alternative and Complementary Medicine; Clinical Autonomic Research;* Dr. Patricia Gerbarg

SURPRISING BENEFITS OF DEEP BREATHING

1. happier mood

Slow breathing activates areas in the brain connected with antidepressive activities, says Luciano Bernardi of the University of Pavia in Italy.

2. deeper sleep

When people with insomnia practiced slow, even breathing for 20 minutes before going to sleep, they woke up fewer times during the night.

3. less anxiety

In a 2015 randomized controlled trial, healthy women who did eight weeks of twice-weekly yoga with breathing exercises significantly reduced anxiety. (A control group did not.)

4. healthier heart

In one small recent study, slow-breathing sessions for 30 minutes a day reduced blood pressure in people with hypertension—and the effect persisted a month later.

5. better air intake

Breathing slowly helps you take in more oxygen. In one study, breathing exercises done several times each day increased oxygen consumption by 37%.

GET IN THE SLEEP ZONE

Surprise: the secret to more restful nights may be rethinking how you spend your days

By Brooke Hauser

SLEEP IS THE BEST MEDITATION," THE DALAI LAMA FAmously said. Of course, not everyone has the discipline of a monk who once shared that he went to bed at 10 p.m., following an evening of prayer and tinkering with wristwatch parts, but we can all be more mindful when it comes to getting a good night's sleep.

According to the Centers for Disease Control and Prevention, between 50 million and 70 million adults in the U.S. have a sleep or wakefulness disorder—the issue is so large-scale that it is considered a public-health problem. Insufficient shut-eye has been linked to car crashes (with tired drivers nodding off at the wheel) and chronic diseases ranging from diabetes to depression. A growing awareness of such risks has led the CDC to suggest sleep hygiene tips, such as setting a consistent bedtime and avoiding consuming too much caffeine.

But cutting down on your coffee intake isn't always enough to court Hypnos, the god of sleep, at a reasonable hour. Just as important as changing your habits is tweaking your mind-set, says Rubin Naiman, a clinical psychologist specializing in integrative sleep and dream medicine. "We assume

that sleep goes off and on like a light switch: I'm awake, and then I'm asleep. It's a common saying that a good sleeper 'goes out like a light,' which is actually not true," he points out.

In actuality, sleeping and waking are bedfellows, so to speak, and Naiman encourages people to tune in to their sleepiness when it's present during the day rather than fight it off with five-hour-energy drinks—and risk developing a negative association with it. "Don't judge it. [Make] a deal with it, saying, 'Listen, I really appreciate your coming. Can you come back later tonight?' " he says. "Sleep is an experience, and it's important to start with that notion. Even though we try to measure it, it's like trying to measure love. It's more like a feeling than it is a fact."

> **"A lot of people aren't sleeping because they are completely sedentary during the day."**

FIND YOUR SLUGGISH TIME
It's also extremely personal. At her clinical practice at the Chopra Center in Carlsbad, Calif., integrative-medicine doctor Valencia Porter helps her patients customize their own power-down experiences. "The first step is to create a daily routine that's going to be more conducive to sleep," says Porter, who begins by asking people what time they go to bed. "According to Ayurveda, between 6 and 10 p.m. is 'kapha time,' which is characterized by a heaviness, a sluggishness, and so it's a natural time for things to wind down. If you looked in nature, the birds would start not chirping as much, and animals, unless they're nocturnal, are going to start finding someplace to sleep. So there's this natural window where, generally by 10, people should be asleep."

BUILD A BETTER RITUAL
If someone reports going to bed later than 10 p.m., Porter suggests moving the time earlier by increments of 15 minutes a week. She also encourages eating a light meal (avoid fatty and sugary foods) at least two hours before bedtime, shutting off all screens one hour before and establishing a low-key eve-

ning routine. Instead of posting that late-night Grumpy Cat meme on Facebook, try taking a warm bath or shower—the coolness that follows is actually a trigger for zzzs—and experimenting with aromatherapy. Lavender and chamomile are especially soothing. Give yourself a massage. Do some gentle stretching and yoga moves, such as child's pose.

Or get into the relaxing ritual of making herbal tea. "Take some time to download, either through journaling or a practice called recapitulation, where you sit quietly and you observe your day," Porter says. "Not judging, not trying to rehash, but just observing seems to help people let go."

HAVE MORE FUN
What you do earlier in the day is also significant. "There's a strong relationship between the depth of our sleep at night and the heights of our passions during the day," Naiman says. "The more fulfilled you feel—the more you feel that you've met your goals, the more awake you are, the more energy you burn during the day in a positive sense—the better the slope that will grind us down into sleep at night." In other words, being happy helps.

GET GROUNDED
Porter recommends getting back to nature by gardening or "grounding," literally connecting one's bare feet with the ground or soil. She recalls one patient, a frazzled Canadian entrepreneur, who took her advice in the middle of winter. "Well, I didn't realize he would go back to Canada and stick his feet in the snow, the icy cold earth. But he enjoyed it, and he kept it up and became really into barefoot running. He felt a powerful connection with the earth," she says. "Grounding for 10 to 20 minutes a day can be helpful for anxiety and depression and subsequently things like insomnia."

If you're not into the idea of going barefoot, try hiking, biking or swimming—any form of

"Grounding," the practice of literally connecting one's bare feet with the earth, may help with depression, anxiety and insomnia.

exercise. "A lot of people aren't sleeping because they are completely sedentary all day," says Robin Berzin, a functional-medicine physician who specializes in high-tech holistic medicine at her practice, Parsley Health. "We evolved to move and jump and run and lift." So if you're not working out, that just might be why you're tossing and turning.

SEE THE LIGHT OF DAY
Another essential: spending more time outdoors in natural light. Several studies, including one at Harvard, have shown that too much artificial light throws off the body's circadian biological clock, which regulates sleepiness and wakefulness throughout the day. Blue light emanating from screens and energy-efficient bulbs is especially harmful, strongly suppressing the secretion of melatonin, a hormone that affects circadian rhythms.

"One of my top tips for getting better sleep at night is getting an app on your phone and your computer that filters out the blue light from the screens over the course of the day so that your circadian rhythms aren't interrupted," says Berzin, who likes one called F.lux. She also uses apps for meditating, such as Headspace and Calm. "A lot of people have

high evening cortisol either because they're working out or working in the evening, and they're stressed," she adds. "I've definitely had a patient come in who has racing thoughts and is really just kind of wired at night—wired and tired. We prescribed a meditation app for 10 minutes in the evening. Technology's our friend, not our foe, but I think we need to learn how to use it to our advantage and to help promote health and well-being."

Still, sometimes the best path to mindfulness is a certain amount of mindlessness, at least right before bedtime. "You don't want to be doing your taxes or trying to figure out your business plan," Porter says. "Do something where you're not really engaging your brain in the hard problems. If you're going to watch TV, watch something lighthearted, not *Frontline* or those shows that really grip you and compel you."

Better to listen to the popular podcast *Sleep with Me*, which lulls listeners with boring bedtime stories and tedious TV-show recaps. Or take a page from the best-selling children's book *The Rabbit Who Wants to Fall Asleep*, which has been said to hypnotize even the most restless rug rat. You may not be out like a light, but you just might sleep like a baby.

Om for Kids

Mindfulness and meditation exercises are helping the next generation get an edge in the classroom

BY MANDY OAKLANDER

ANY TEACHER WHO'S EVER PRODDED, begged or bribed a child to sit still and listen knows there aren't a ton of proven ways to get a kid to tune in. But new research offers a different suggestion: breathe. Not you—them.

Mindfulness and meditation programs are emerging as powerful ways to calm down kids, sharpen their brain and make them kinder to their classmates. The many techniques appear to work in kids who are so young, they've yet to meet their first fraction. In an ongoing study at the University of North Carolina at Wilmington, scientists are teaching preschoolers yoga poses and meditations, and after just two weeks of practice, these kids have better attention, awareness, gratitude and happiness compared with a control group of children. "What's amazing is that this brief exposure appears to be so powerful," says lead researcher Simone Nguyen, a developmental-psychology professor at the university. "A few minutes of breathing, a few minutes of paying attention to the moment are appearing to make a difference." Children tend to be more open-minded than adults and less entrenched in habits—smartphones, social media—that distract from the present moment, Nguyen adds.

Techniques like these seem to work for kids all the way up to high school seniors. Other research hints that Transcendental Meditation leads to improved graduation rates: 15% higher, one study found. Seemingly idle time may have a place at school after all.

Sources: *Developmental Psychology*; *Education*; *Journal of Positive Psychology*; David Lynch Foundation; *British Journal of Psychiatry*; *Journal of Child and Family Studies*

Here's what the science says:

MORE KINDNESS
Fourth- and fifth-graders who participated in a mindfulness and kindness program showed better social behavior than their peers and were less aggressive and better liked.

BETTER MATH SCORES
The mindful group had math scores 15% higher than their peers'. In a separate study, 41% of meditating middle schoolers gained at least one level in math on a state standardized test.

Morning breather: A behavior-intervention teacher leads Minnesota elementary school students in yoga.

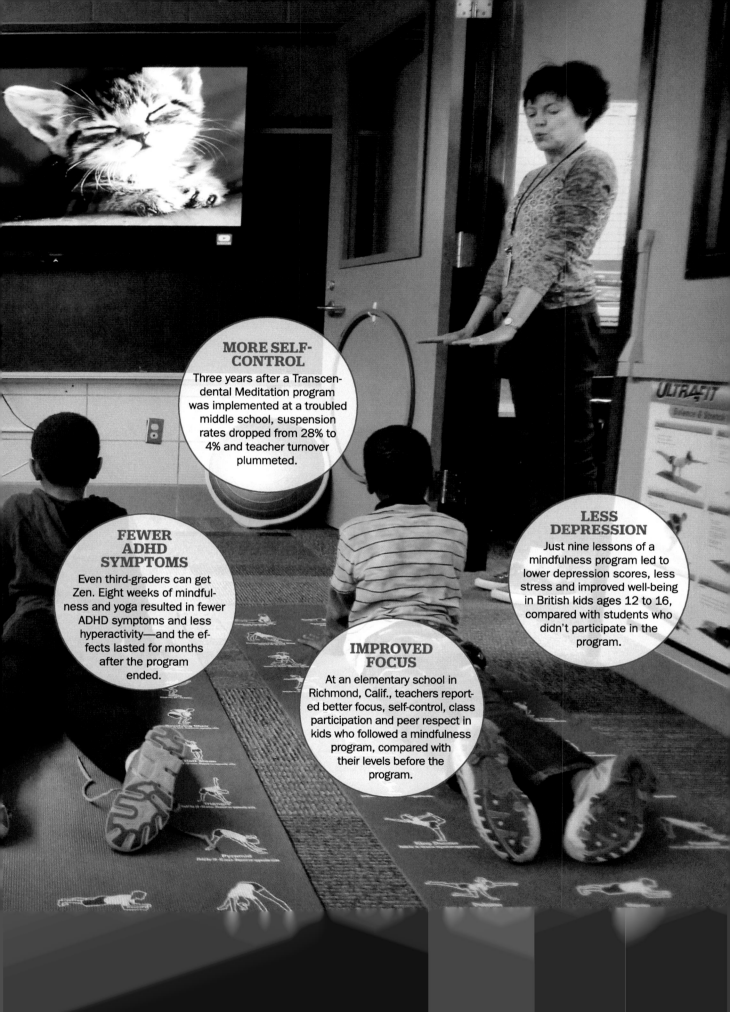

MORE SELF-CONTROL

Three years after a Transcendental Meditation program was implemented at a troubled middle school, suspension rates dropped from 28% to 4% and teacher turnover plummeted.

FEWER ADHD SYMPTOMS

Even third-graders can get Zen. Eight weeks of mindfulness and yoga resulted in fewer ADHD symptoms and less hyperactivity—and the effects lasted for months after the program ended.

IMPROVED FOCUS

At an elementary school in Richmond, Calif., teachers reported better focus, self-control, class participation and peer respect in kids who followed a mindfulness program, compared with their levels before the program.

LESS DEPRESSION

Just nine lessons of a mindfulness program led to lower depression scores, less stress and improved well-being in British kids ages 12 to 16, compared with students who didn't participate in the program.

CAN YOU THINK YOURSELF WELL?

One doctor explains how to tap into the power
of your mind to feel better—every day

By Lissa Rankin, M.D.

 HAT IF YOU HAD THE ABILITY TO HEAL YOUR BODY JUST BY changing how you think and feel? I know it sounds radical, coming from a doctor. When people are doing everything "right"—eating veggies, avoiding red meat and processed foods, exercising, sleeping well and so forth—we should expect them to live long, prosperous lives and die of old age while peacefully slumbering, right? So why is it that so many health nuts are sicker than other people who pig out, guzzle beer and park in front of the TV?

I consider myself one of those health nuts. I drink my green juice, take my vitamins, hike and practice yoga daily, get good sleep, see a doctor and avoid harmful toxins. Yet I have come to believe that the purely physical realm of illness—the part you can diagnose with laboratory tests—is only

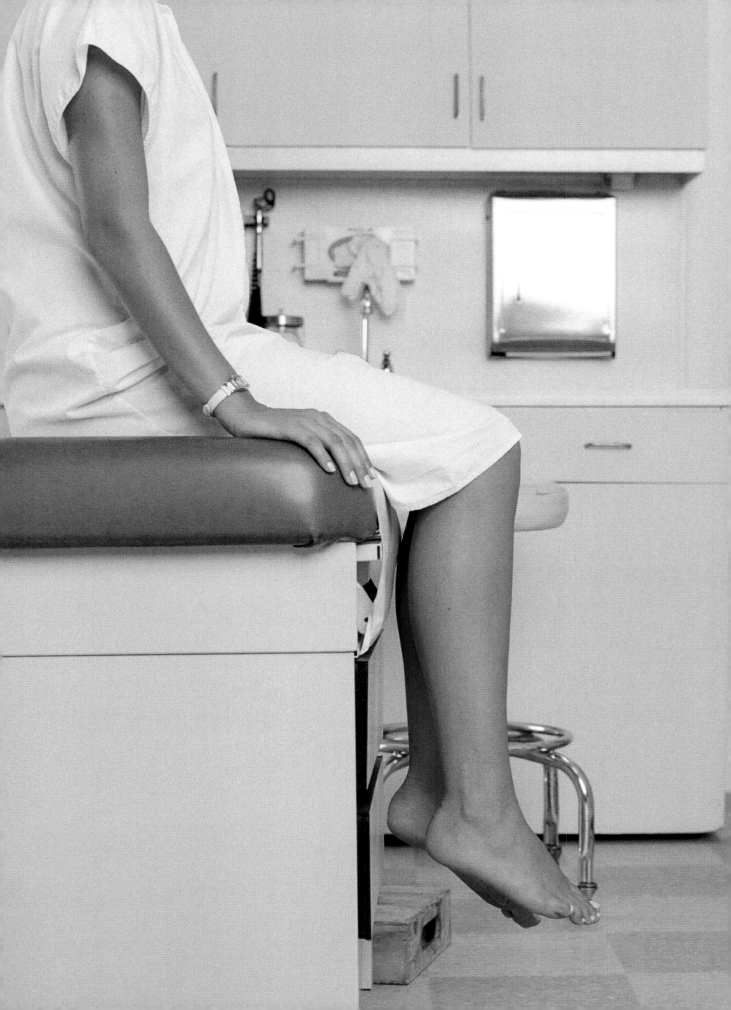

part of the equation. It's a big part, mind you, but not the whole shebang. My experience with patients (as well as my personal background) has led me to the conclusion that whether they become sick or stay healthy, as well as whether they remain ill or manage to heal themselves, might have more to do with everything else that's going on in their lives than with any specific health standard they abide by.

When healthy habits aren't enough

Eight years ago, I started working in an integrative medicine practice. My new patients were some of the most health-conscious people I've ever had the privilege to serve. Many of them ate a vegan diet, worked out, slept soundly each night and took vitamins every morning. But some of them were also mysteriously sick, complaining of fatigue, aches, gastrointestinal disturbances and other symptoms. I was baffled! I ran batteries of tests, and occasionally I would pick up something that eventually resulted in the complete resolution of a patient's symptoms. But more often than not, I would find nothing.

I was really motivated to solve the puzzle of why these "healthy" patients were so sick. Instead of focusing exclusively on physician-recommended behaviors, medical history and

Your feel-great checklist

1. Healthy relationships, including a strong network of family, friends, loved ones and colleagues

2. A healthy, meaningful way to spend your days, whether or not you work outside the home

3. A healthy creative life, spiritual life and sexual life, as well as a healthy financial life that allows you to meet all your essential needs

4. A healthy mental and emotional life, characterized by optimism and happiness and free of fear, anxiety, depression and other mental-health ailments

5. A healthy lifestyle that supports the physical health of the body with good nutrition, regular exercise, adequate sleep and avoidance of unhealthy addictions

6. A healthy living environment, free of toxins, radiation and natural-disaster hazards

other traditional factors, I dug deep into their personal lives. I asked them questions: "What do you love about yourself? What's missing from your life? What do you appreciate about your life? Are you in a romantic relationship? If so, are you happy? If not, do you wish you were? Are you fulfilled at work? Do you feel like you're in touch with your life's purpose? Do you feel sexually satisfied? Do you express yourself creatively? Do you feel financially stable, or are you stressed about money? If your fairy godmother could change one thing about your life, what would you wish for?"

My patients' answers often gave me more insight into why they might be sick than any lab test or exam could. They were unhealthy not because of bad genes or poor habits or rotten luck but because they were lonely or miserable in their relationships, stressed about work, freaked out about their finances or profoundly depressed.

On the flip side, I had other patients who ate junk, forgot to take their supplements, rarely exercised and enjoyed seemingly perfect health. Their responses revealed that their lives were filled with love, fun, meaningful work, creative expression, spiritual connection and other traits that differentiated them from the sick health enthusiasts.

What's really going on?

That's when I narrowed it down to two questions I would ask patients at their appointments: "What do you think might lie at the root of your illness?" and "What does your body need in order to heal?" Occasionally, they answered with conventional health-related insights, saying, "I need an antidepressant" or "I need to lose 20 pounds." But more often than not, they said introspective things, like "I hate my job," "I need more 'me' time," "I must divorce my spouse," "I have to finish my novel," "I need to hire a nanny," "I need to make more friends," "I need to forgive myself," "I need to love myself" or "I need to stop being such a pessimist." Whoa.

Although many patients weren't ready to do what their intuition told them their bodies needed, my bravest patients made radical changes. Some quit their jobs. Others left their marriages. Some moved to new cities or towns. Others pursued long-suppressed dreams. The results these patients achieved were astonishing. Sometimes, a list of illnesses would disappear, often quickly. Even smaller steps, like talking to a boss about workplace problems or seeing a marriage counselor, helped. I was in awe.

But I shouldn't have been surprised: I had healed myself in much the same way. By the time I was in my 20s, I had been diagnosed with multiple health conditions, including high blood pressure and precancerous changes on my cervix. At 33, I was burned out, owing to my career in a busy obstetrics and gynecology practice. I wound up leaving my job, selling my house and liquidating my retirement account. My husband, our baby and I moved from chaotic San Diego to a small, sleepy town in Northern California, where I spent two years digging into the root causes of my illness, diagnosing what needed to be changed and mustering up the courage to take action. As a result, my health conditions either completely resolved or drastically improved.

The mind/ body Rx

This is not "woo woo" metaphysics here. The scientific evidence I have uncovered in major medical journals backs this up: the lifestyle choices you make can optimize your body's relaxation response, counteract the stress response and result in physiological changes, leading to better health. The body doesn't fuel how we live our lives. Instead, it is a mirror of how we live our lives. So if you're not feeling well despite doing all the "right" things, take a deep breath and ask yourself: What do I think might lie at the root of my illness? What does my body need in order to heal? If you're honest with yourself, the answers could save your health—and your life.

Adapted from Mind Over Medicine: Scientific Proof That You Can Heal Yourself, *by Lissa Rankin, M.D. (Hay House, May 2013). Rankin is a physician in Marin County, California.*

DEVICES MESS WITH YOUR BRAIN . . .

Is your smartphone affecting your mind?
Yes—and you're probably suffering from
phantom text syndrome, too

By Markham Heid

IRST IT WAS RADIO. THEN IT WAS TELEVISION. NOW DOOM-sayers are offering scary predictions about the consequences of smartphones and all the other digital devices to which we've all grown so attached. So why should you pay any attention to the warnings this time?

Apart from portability, the big difference between something like a traditional TV and your tablet is the social component, says David Strayer, a professor of cognition and neural science at the University of Utah. "Through Twitter or Facebook or email, someone in your social network is contacting you in some way all the time," Strayer says.

"We're inherently social organisms," adds Paul Atchley, a cognitive psychologist at the University of Kansas. There's almost nothing more compelling than social information, he says, which activates part of your brain's

Experts say silencing your smartphone or setting it to deliver new emails only every 30 minutes are ways to combat the negative effects of our devices.

reward system. Your noodle is also hardwired to respond to novel sights and sounds. (For most of human history, a sudden noise might have signaled the presence of a predator.) "So something like a buzz or beep or flashing light is tapping into that threat-detection system," he explains.

Combine that sudden beep with the implicit promise of new social info, and you have a near-perfect, unignorable stimulus that will pull your focus away from whatever task your

brain is working on. And although you may think you can quickly check a text or email and pick up the task where you left off, you really can't.

"Every time you switch your focus from one thing to another, there's something called a switch cost," says Earl Miller, a professor of neuroscience at MIT. "Your brain stumbles a bit, and it requires time to get back to where it was before it was distracted."

While this isn't a big deal if you're doing

something simple and rote—making an omelet, say, or folding clothes—it can be a very big deal if your brain is trying to sort out a complex problem, Miller says.

ALERT OVERLOAD

One recent study found that it can take your brain 15 to 25 minutes to get back to where it was after stopping to check an email. And Miller's own research shows that you don't get better at this sort of multitasking with practice. In fact, people who judged themselves to be expert digital multitaskers tended to be pretty bad at it, he says.

"You're not able to think as deeply on something when you're being distracted every few minutes," Miller notes. "And thinking deeply is where real insights come from."

There seems to be an easy solution to this: when you're working on something complicated, switch off your phone and email.

That could work for some people. But there's evidence that as your brain becomes accustomed to checking a device every few minutes, it will struggle to stay on task even when it's not interrupted by digital alerts. "There's something called 'phantom text syndrome,' " Atchley says. "You think you hear a text or alert, but there isn't one."

Although phantom texts can afflict adults, Atchley says this phenomenon is pretty much universal among people under the age of 20—many of whom wouldn't recognize a world that doesn't include smartphones. Even if you don't hear phantom alerts, you may still find yourself reflexively wanting to check your device every few minutes for updates, which disrupts your concentration regardless of whether you ignore that impulse.

FINDING FOCUS

Your ability to focus aside, a 2014 study appearing in the journal *PLOS One* found that people who spend a lot of time "media multi-

tasking"—or juggling lots of different websites, apps, programs or other digital stimuli—tend to have less gray matter in a part of their brain involved with thought and emotion control. These same structural changes are associated with obsessive-compulsive disorder, depression and anxiety disorders, says that study's first author, Kep Kee Loh, who conducted his research at University College London.

Atchley says that research suggests that lots of device use bombards your brain's prefrontal cortex, which plays a big role in willpower and decision-making. "The prefrontal cortex prevents us from doing stupid things, whether it's eating junk food or texting while driving," he explains.

He says this part of the human brain isn't "fully wired" until one's early 20s—an issue that has him worried about how heavy device use may be affecting children and adolescents.

So what's the antidote? Spending time in nature may counteract the focus-draining effects of too much tech time, indicates research that Atchley and Strayer published in 2012. Meditation may also offer focus-strengthening benefits.

Strayer says putting your phone on silent and setting your email to deliver new messages only every 30 minutes are ways to use your devices strategically and "not be a slave to them."

Of course, there are plenty of benefits associated with the latest and greatest technologies. Ease and convenience of staying in touch with friends is a big one. But many open questions remain when it comes to the true cost of our digital distractions.

"Imagine Einstein trying to think about mathematics at a time when part of his brain was wondering what was going on with Twitter," Atchley says. "People make incredible breakthroughs when they're concentrating very hard on a specific task, and I wonder if our devices are taking away our ability to do that."

...SO GIVE YOURSELF AN I-BREAK!

A smart, non-extreme guide to powering down more and being present for actual life

By Ellen Seidman

 F RUSSIAN PHYSIOLOGIST IVAN PAVLOV WERE AROUND TO redo his famous experiment, the one in which dogs salivated when a bell that they associated with food rang, he might use humans and a smartphone. I'll bet the results would show that at the sound of every *buzz!*, *ding!* and *ping!*, people would twitch and then grab their phones.

At our house, my smartphone is considered an appendage. My children joke that it's my third ear when I talk on it a lot and my third hand when I text like a fiend. Some days, there's so much incoming info—emails, instant messages, social-media notifications—that I can't even recall which medium I read it on. Did my friend contact me on Facebook? By text? Wha? Some mornings, I wake up and form tweets in my head.

Polls paint a picture of i-dependency: Americans spend 1.7 hours a day social networking and check their phones some 46 times a day. The result is that disconnecting has become both trendy and a mental-health must-do. We can go on tech-free retreats through companies like Digital Detox (motto: "Disconnect to reconnect"). Ironically enough, a new generation of apps has sprung up to help us resist the siren call of technology. Celebrities, meanwhile, proudly announce that they are signing off. As Kerry

Washington recently posted on Instagram, "It's time to take a teeny break from social media. Feeling called to be a bit more quiet and still."

WHY DISCONNECT? SOME MOTIVATION

Obviously, technology makes life easier, more fun and more social—within limits. "Do we want to live an i-life or a real life? That's a choice we have to make," says Orianna Fielding, the founder of the Digital Detox Company and author of *Unplugged: How to Live Mindfully in a Digital World*. "At the end of the day, it's a five-inch piece of hardware with no pulse, and we give it more attention than [we do] people we know."

When we're overly immersed in social media and Googleland, we're missing out on real conversations, thinking deeply and creatively, doing restorative physical activities like biking (you're not texting and biking, right?) and truly connecting with ourselves. One recent study funded by the National Institutes of Health linked high social-media usage to depression. Other research has found that social networking increased people's anxiety both about how they compare with other people . . . and about being away from their devices.

There are health hazards of virtual codependency as well, aside from the dangers of walking into traffic as you check messages. Tech neck is real: one study found that tilting our head forward 60 degrees to peer at our phones puts 60 pounds of pressure on our neck. Vision fatigue and headaches are also side effects, along with lower-quality sleep.

For those who feel that they absolutely cannot disconnect at work, consider that technology can make us less effective workers. "Your productivity will shoot up and you'll give your company much better quality and quantity if you're not always switching between email and your work," says Joanne Cantor, the former outreach director of the Center for Communication Research at the University of Wisconsin–Madison and author of *Conquer CyberOverload*. "The brain can't focus on two things at once, so you're always losing your train of thought." In one study, in the journal *Computers & Education*, students instant-messaged either before, after or while reading an article. Those who did so while reading took significantly longer to get through the piece.

HOW TO POWER DOWN

Truth is, we all know that it would benefit us, body and soul, to disconnect on occasion. But how do we do that in the real world? Here are tricks the experts themselves use to tamp down their tech time.

• Pinpoint the time sucks.

We plop down on the couch, start scrolling through Facebook updates, and suddenly it's two hours later. Where does the Internet time go? You can figure that out with an application like RescueTime, which runs in the background of computers and mobile devices and tracks how much time we spend in certain programs (including email), on websites or in Web browsers. There are free and premium plans. The Moment app, which is free, does the same for iPhones and iPads. Once you've identified the big culprits, you will know where to cut back.

• Ask: Am I truly enjoying my online activity?

If not, find another. When we take a breather at work to glance at Instagram or Pinterest, it's what Laura Vanderkam, the author of *I Know How She Does It: How Successful Women Make the Most of Their Time*, calls a "fake break." As she explains, "These online diversions are not nearly as pleasurable as real-world breaks like talking with someone you like or just taking a walk." Not to mention the guilt we feel for not, say, crafting capes for a child's birthday party—call it Pintstress.

• Put yourself in airplane mode.

Finding realistic tech-free periods is key to success, and bedtime is a good place to start. The problem is that too many of us are charging our phones on a nightstand or using them as alarms. One survey by the National Sleep Foundation found that 71% of adults have a smartphone, tablet or computer in the bedroom—and close to half keep them on. "If you're an alcoholic trying hard not to drink, you don't have open bottles of liquor on the table. Keep the temptation away," says Cantor. Do the old-school thing: get an alarm clock, and plug that phone in somewhere else—perhaps in another part of your home, as Cantor does.

• **Do a digital sabbath.**
That's the term for giving devices a rest for 24 hours over a weekend. Entrepreneur Claire Diaz-Ortiz, one of Twitter's first employees and the author of *Design Your Day*, takes it one step further by closing her computer Friday after work and not opening it again till Monday morning. "Having it shut off means I can't run in and check email for five minutes on Saturday morning—it requires booting up, which makes it harder to do," she says.

• **Manage your email. Don't let it manage you.**
"One of the challenges with email is it makes you accountable to other people's priorities and what they think is urgent," notes Diaz-Ortiz. After realizing how much of her life was spent dealing with email—so much so, she says, "that I couldn't be thinking about what I was doing in the moment, whether at the pediatrician's or watching *The Bachelor*"—she deleted email capabilities from her phone. She checks it on a laptop twice a day, in the hour before lunch and then before shutting down at the end of the day. People know to text her for anything urgent.

A less drastic route: set up a dedicated email address for family or an assistant or boss, so that those are the only emails that come to a phone. With texting, put the Do Not Disturb function in iPhone settings to use: flick it on, and then choose a few people whose texts can come through.

> Do a digital sabbath. That's the term for giving devices a rest for 24 hours over a weekend.

• **Swap in something fun.**
When we're trying to get rid of a habit, we have more success if we replace it with a better one, says Cantor. "So don't just say, 'I won't check Facebook tonight,' " she urges. "Tell yourself, 'I'm going to call an old friend and have a long talk.' "

• **Get a digital babysitter.**
The popular Freedom app works as a Web, social-media and app blocker. Digital Detach for Android limits everything except calls and texts for a set period of time. StayFocusd is a Google Chrome extension that helps beat Internet procrastination by blocking websites or limiting usage of them; SelfControl does the same for Macs.

• **Try phone stacking.**
To combat the unfortunate phenomenon of being out with friends or colleagues who are all glued to their mobiles, people are playing a game known as phone stacking, in which everyone places their device in the center of the table, and the first person to go for theirs pays for the meal. Businesswoman and technology blue blood Randi Zuckerberg plays this variation at home with phones: "The person who reaches for it first does the dishes."

• **Don't carry it everywhere.**
"Every time your phone buzzes, it creates a buzz of excitement—maybe it's that friend! Maybe it's that job offer!—that's hard to resist," says Brian Primack, director of the Center for Research on Media, Technology and Health at the University of Pittsburgh. Sure, we could turn off the alerts—but that doesn't turn off temptation, as Primack discovered when he'd check email every time he went to the office coffee machine. His solution: a phone holder he keeps off his desk. "Now when I go to get coffee," he says, "I don't take my phone, and I try to be in the moment."

• **Download permission to unplug.**
Going offline at work can be anxiety-provoking—we don't want to appear unavailable to the powers that be, notes Fielding: "Employees tell me that they crave the legitimate right to unplug." These days, when she takes time offline, she sets an out-of-office reply that reads, "I am unplugged, connecting with the people and world around me, and I'll get back to you as soon as I'm reconnected." As she enthusiastically says, "There's such freedom in that! People who see it tell me, 'I'm so jealous,' and I say, 'You can do it too!' "

PART TWO

Find Your Center

THE ART OF MEDITATION

Meditation has gone from fringe ritual to mainstream health move. But can modern-day multitaskers really learn to quiet their minds?

By Jancee Dunn

T'LL CHANGE YOUR LIFE!" MY trendier friends say. For the past year, they have been urging me to meditate. "Not my thing," I answer. I'm not good at Zen; I'm good at running late to an appointment as I fire off five texts. But after a particularly chaotic week in which I reeled from work crisis to kid crisis—feeling panicky, my mind whirring nonstop—I decided to try it out. It's not as if meditation has any weird side effects or causes injuries. It doesn't require any gear (like my failed cycling venture) or an expensive trainer. So why not give it a go?

Although I couldn't care less about being on-trend, meditation is having a moment. Katy Perry reportedly does a 20-minute session every morning ("the only time my mind gets absolute rest"). Hugh Jackman, who actually sits in stillness with his two children, has said that the ritual changed his life. Actress Jordana Brewster meditates on set. It's become a go-to stress reducer for powerhouses Arianna Huffington and Oprah Winfrey, both of whom have offered classes to their employees.

Meditation used to be viewed as a self-involved exercise done by, as devotee Russell Brand put it, "weird old hippies." But that perception has vanished thanks to an avalanche of research on the ritual's benefits: it can reduce stress, lower blood pressure, slow Alzheimer's and curb tobacco cravings. One major review from Johns Hopkins University showed that mindfulness meditation may be just as effective as antidepressants for treating anxiety symptoms.

I couldn't imagine finding the time to make meditation a daily thing—but oddly enough, that's what happened.

OK, DEEP BREATH

Hindus have meditated for thousands of years. In fact, forms of the practice have been used in most of the world's major religions. But it wasn't until Transcendental Meditation's popularity surged in the West in the '70s that scientists started paying attention to its array of health benefits. Known as TM, Transcendental Meditation involves closing your eyes and repeating a mantra to free the mind from conscious thought.

Another popular form of meditation, mindfulness, is also gaining steam among health experts. Doctors at prominent hospitals regularly recommend it for conditions like insomnia and irritable bowel syndrome. All you need to do is pay attention to your inner and outer experience in the present moment, without judgment. Like TM, it has been shown to decrease stress within eight weeks. I decided to try it. But first, I consulted a few experts for guidance.

Ideally, you get mindful in a quiet spot—although it can be done while walking, sitting at your desk at work or even standing in a long line at the grocery store. It's more important to be away from engaging distractions, such as your computer, say experts, than it is for your space to be dead silent. "Close your eyes or not, however you feel most at ease," advises Sharon Salzberg, co-founder of the Insight Meditation Society in Barre, Mass. "Settle your attention on the feeling of the normal, natural breath, wherever it's most clear to you—the nostrils, chest or abdomen. See if you can feel one breath fully. Then the next breath." It's that simple.

I sat on my couch with my legs folded, closed my eyes and breathed. In. Out. Soon I felt calmer in my body, but my mind was buzzing with not-very-chill thoughts about a friend who never stops talking about her boyfriend. Perfectly normal, says Salzberg: "It's a common belief that to meditate successfully, you have to wipe all thoughts from your mind. That's unlikely to happen, and it's not the goal anyway."

When you find your mind wandering, the experts say to notice the thoughts and then just let them go. Gently bring your attention back

> **When you find your mind wandering, the experts say, notice the thoughts and then let them go.**

How Meditation Changes Your Body

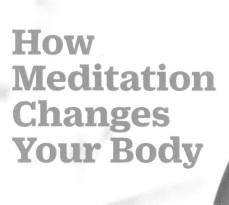

PAIN DIMINISHES
It appears to change activity in key pain-processing regions of the brain—in one study, meditators experienced a 40% reduction in pain intensity.

YOUR BRAIN RELEASES HAPPY CHEMICALS
You get a boost of serotonin, dopamine and endorphins, all linked to a good mood.

SWELLING SUBSIDES
It can reduce stress-induced inflammation from inflammatory conditions such as arthritis and asthma.

BLOOD PRESSURE DROPS
And the effect isn't just temporary: a Medical College of Wisconsin study showed that people who meditated twice a day for 20 minutes lowered their blood pressure by 5 mm Hg.

DIGESTION RUNS MORE SMOOTHLY
Stress triggers the stomach-churning fight-or-flight instinct, shutting down digestion. When relaxed, the body reboots the parasympathetic nervous system, which gets digestion flowing.

to the present and your breathing. I started with 10 minutes, setting an alarm on my phone (soft church bells, in keeping with the mood). I had to refocus on breathing six or seven times; I guess that's why they call it a practice. At the end of my session, though, I felt as if I had awoken from a refreshing nap. The point is not to go into a trancelike state or to be visited by wondrous, life-changing thoughts but rather to enter a state of relaxed alertness.

"It's ideal to make meditation a daily part of your routine, even if you begin with 5 or 10 minutes," says Hugh Byrne, a senior teacher with the Insight Meditation Community of Washington, D.C. He recommends working up to at least 30 minutes. That proved impossible for me, though it was amazing how much time I freed up when I didn't go online shoe shopping. Yes, I'm perpetually busy, but it's not like I'm the secretary of state.

SERENITY NOW

By week three, I was able to get in the zone faster. I went on for 20 minutes, as does the hip-hop mogul Russell Simmons, author of the book *Success Through Stillness: Meditation Made Simple*. "Starting off my day without meditation would be like going to work without brushing my teeth," he says.

Although I'm not that committed, I have grown to love the refreshed and clear feeling that carries over throughout the day. I don't feel as overwhelmed. As many studies show, meditation elicits a physiological reaction that actually dampens your stress response [see "How Meditation Changes Your Body," preceding page]. Now when I'm in a nerve-racking situation, I can notice it with a bit of detachment, which helps me take action.

I like to do 10 minutes before or after an event that makes me twitchy, like a dentist appointment or a conversation with my accountant. Training myself to refocus my thoughts on the right now has improved my concentration as well. It's not that my stress has magically vanished; I still have little control over, for example, work deadlines, the IRS or teeth cleanings. But I do have more of a handle on how I feel. Plus, if I ever run into Hugh Jackman at a party, we'll have something to talk about.

A Five-Minute Meditation

You don't need endless free time to find your center. This streamlined routine gets the job done

BY SHARON LIAO

WE KNOW, WE KNOW. YOU'RE TOO wound up to meditate. You don't have time. It's not your thing. But before you roll your eyes and get back to doing 18 things at once, consider this: a study published in April 2013 in *Social Cognitive and Affective Neuroscience* reported that the practice can reduce anxiety levels by up to 22%. Research has also suggested that meditating can actually form new and permanent neural connections in the brain. "Meditation trains your mind to focus on the moment instead of worrying about what occurred in the past or what could happen in the future," says Janet Nima Taylor, an American Buddhist nun in Kansas City, Mo., and the author of *Meditation for Nonmeditators*. The amazing thing? All you need is five minutes a day. "Anyone can do it, and the more consistent you are, the easier it will become," says Taylor, who devised the routine on this page. So take a timer, a notepad and a pen to a quiet room with soft (but not dim) lighting. Sit up straight in a comfortable chair, remove your shoes and socks and get started.

> "Anyone can do it, and the more consistent you are, the easier it will become."

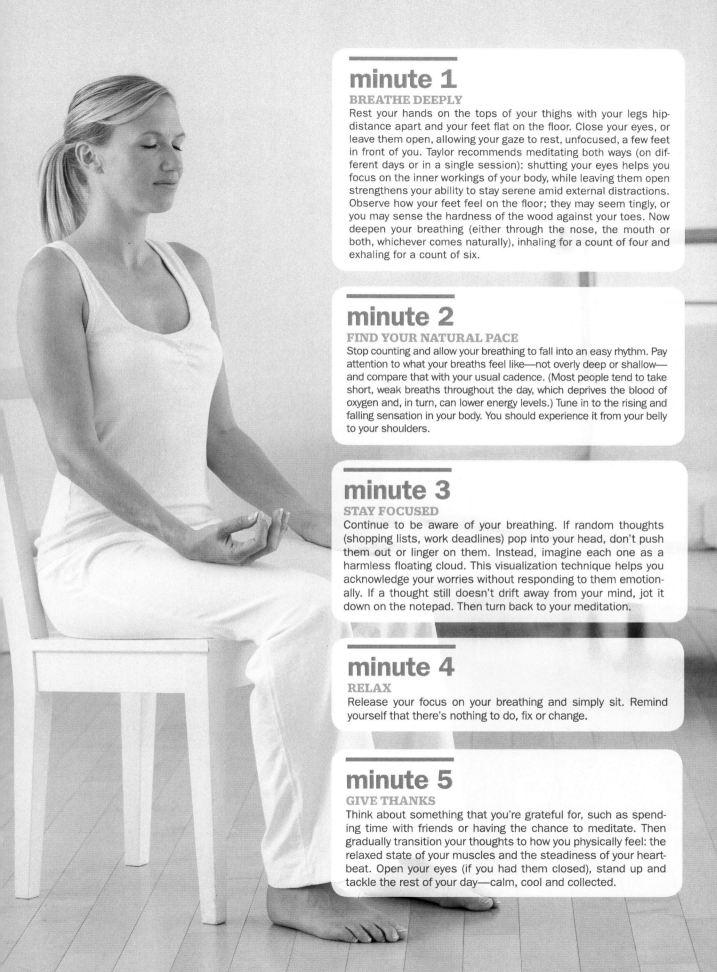

minute 1
BREATHE DEEPLY

Rest your hands on the tops of your thighs with your legs hip-distance apart and your feet flat on the floor. Close your eyes, or leave them open, allowing your gaze to rest, unfocused, a few feet in front of you. Taylor recommends meditating both ways (on different days or in a single session): shutting your eyes helps you focus on the inner workings of your body, while leaving them open strengthens your ability to stay serene amid external distractions. Observe how your feet feel on the floor; they may seem tingly, or you may sense the hardness of the wood against your toes. Now deepen your breathing (either through the nose, the mouth or both, whichever comes naturally), inhaling for a count of four and exhaling for a count of six.

minute 2
FIND YOUR NATURAL PACE

Stop counting and allow your breathing to fall into an easy rhythm. Pay attention to what your breaths feel like—not overly deep or shallow—and compare that with your usual cadence. (Most people tend to take short, weak breaths throughout the day, which deprives the blood of oxygen and, in turn, can lower energy levels.) Tune in to the rising and falling sensation in your body. You should experience it from your belly to your shoulders.

minute 3
STAY FOCUSED

Continue to be aware of your breathing. If random thoughts (shopping lists, work deadlines) pop into your head, don't push them out or linger on them. Instead, imagine each one as a harmless floating cloud. This visualization technique helps you acknowledge your worries without responding to them emotionally. If a thought still doesn't drift away from your mind, jot it down on the notepad. Then turn back to your meditation.

minute 4
RELAX

Release your focus on your breathing and simply sit. Remind yourself that there's nothing to do, fix or change.

minute 5
GIVE THANKS

Think about something that you're grateful for, such as spending time with friends or having the chance to meditate. Then gradually transition your thoughts to how you physically feel: the relaxed state of your muscles and the steadiness of your heartbeat. Open your eyes (if you had them closed), stand up and tackle the rest of your day—calm, cool and collected.

Meditation Made Mobile: On-the-Go Apps

No, seriously: these downloads turn your iPhone into a pocket mindfulness coach

BY JACQUELINE ANDRIAKOS

BELIEVE IT: THE GADGET THAT NURTURES your emoji and Instagram obsessions can also provide you with a daily dose of Zen. Meditation apps provide both the total newbie and the practiced pro convenient instruction, says Sharon Salzberg, a meditation teacher and co-founder of the Insight Meditation Society in Massachusetts. "All of us can use the little reminders or sense of community that these apps provide as we're trying to maintain a regular practice in our hectic lives," she explains. Even Apple is getting in on the movement: the next version of the Apple Watch (out in fall 2016) will feature a mindfulness app called Breathe. But you don't need a wired watch to calm your body—choose the smartphone app here that best fits your need, schedule and level of experience.

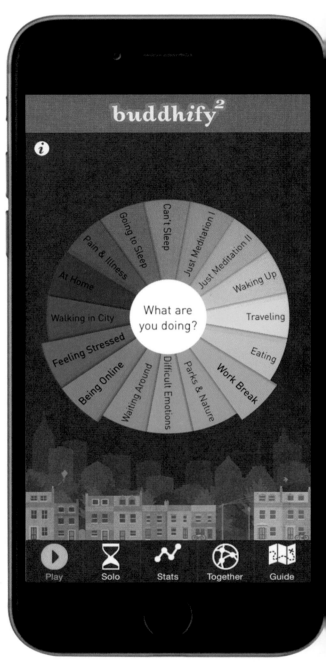

If you're a crazed commuter

TRY: BUDDHIFY

On a flight? Between meetings? Hustling through city streets? The Buddhify app gives mindfulness a modern, metropolitan edge, with bright graphics and solo or guided meditations you can do during the most chaotic junctures in life—even those you would never have imagined could be transformed into a peaceful moment. ($4.99 on iTunes and Google Play)

If you're a busy beginner

TRY: HEADSPACE

Created by a trained Tibetan Buddhist monk, the website and app require you to first complete a free 10-day introductory meditation program before you can access additional content packs, including a series designed for improving relationships and your health. Bonus: the intro course takes only 10 minutes per day. (Free on iTunes and Google Play; memberships start at $12.95 per month)

If you need a mini escape

TRY: CALM

Calm.com helps you break from the confines of your day-to-day. In the app version, the program guides you through a few long, deep breaths before you can explore further. Whether your happy place is sitting beside a crackling fireplace or staring out into a coastline sunset, you can customize the background scenery and noise to make it a virtual retreat. Opt for guided sessions—some free, some for a fee—or a solo go-around using the timer. (Free on iTunes and Google Play; subscriptions start at $3.99 per month)

If you like to mix things up

TRY: WHIL

Whil—created by the founders of the yoga line Lululemon—allows you to power down your mind or train your body with traditional guided meditation practices, as well as video yoga sessions. Take the guesswork out of picking a practice with the WhilPower feature: you input your mood, your intention and the amount of time you can spare, and the app combs through its database and IDs the most fitting option. (Free on iTunes and Google Play)

If you're a master meditator

TRY: INSIGHT TIMER

Tune up your training session by choosing your preferred interval time, ending bell sound and ambient noise. On the app's welcome screen, you can also see in real time who else in the Insight Timer community around the world is deep into a mindfulness session. (Free on iTunes and Google Play)

Peace, Love and Popcorn

In big-screen hits and favorite TV shows, pop culture keeps serving up lessons in finding your center. Here's a sampling from the past few decades

BY ANDRÉA FORD

STAR WARS: THE EMPIRE STRIKES BACK (1980)

The *Star Wars* franchise is flush with references to mindful living, and is there any fictional character more present than Yoda? "You must unlearn what you have learned," the proverb-spouting Jedi master (voiced by Frank Oz) tells a frustrated Luke (Mark Hamill) before explaining the Force: "Life creates it, makes it grow. Its energy surrounds us and binds us. Luminous beings are we."

1970   1980   1990

THE KARATE KID (1984)

When young Daniel (Ralph Macchio) complains to his mentor, Mr. Miyagi (Pat Morita), that his "whole life is going out of focus," his teacher calmly tells him, "When you feel life out of focus, always return to basic of life," as he folds his hands in front of him. "What, praying?" Daniel asks skeptically. "Breathing," Miyagi responds.

GROUNDHOG DAY (1993)

Cynical, self-centered weatherman Phil (Bill Murray) is forced to live intensely in the present moment—or the present day—over and over again. At first he does this recklessly, but, as time fails to go on, he begins to act with abundant compassion for others. The film explores a journey of getting "unstuck" through awareness and kindness. Perhaps Harold Ramis, the film's director and co-writer, lifted some themes from his personal practice of Zen Buddhism.

THE BIG LEBOWSKI (1998)

The Dude (Jeff Bridges) is the embodiment of "going with the flow." Despite a weakness for White Russians, he approaches life in a decidedly mindful way. His signature line, "The Dude abides," has inspired countless fans to interpret the meaning; it later motivated Bridges to write a book titled *The Dude and the Zen Master* (2013). In 2015, Bridges even released an album of his own guided meditations, *Sleeping Tapes*. On one track, he spends nearly three minutes making otherworldly humming sounds.

MAD MEN (2015)

In the final scene of the final episode, Don Draper (Jon Hamm) is at a seaside retreat. As he sits in lotus position on a magnificent cliff with a guru and other soul searchers, a bell rings, and they recite the mantra *om*. The bell rings again, and Don smiles serenely. Coke's iconic 1971 "hilltop ad" featuring "I'd Like to Buy the World a Coke" plays. Did our dark hero reach a higher plane of existence—or just figure out a way to cash in on the zeitgeist?

2000   2010   2020

I HEART HUCKABEES (2004)

A quirky pair of "existential detectives" investigate people's lives to help them make personal discoveries. In explaining the philosophy to a new client, Albert (Jason Schwartzman), Bernard (Dustin Hoffman) uses a blanket to symbolize the interconnectedness of everything. "We need to learn how to see the blanket truth all the time, right in the everyday stuff," he says. "When you get the blanket thing, you can relax, because everything you could ever want or be, you already have and are." A mindful idea, indeed.

PARKS AND RECREATION (2012)

In a season-four episode, the holistically obsessed Chris (Rob Lowe) asks Ron (Nick Offerman) to join him at a meditation studio, where Ron insists on standing and is baffled by the practice. Afterward, Chris remarks, "You radiated mindfulness! What were you thinking about?" When Ron stoically tells him he wasn't thinking at all, Chris laments that he struggles to achieve that "clear head space" no matter how hard he tries. Ron's response: "Don't try so hard."

INSIDE OUT (2015)

Preteen Riley (Kaitlyn Dias) has been uprooted from her happy home in Minnesota to San Francisco. Within her mind, the personified emotions Joy (Amy Poehler), Sadness (Phyllis Smith), Fear (Bill Hader), Anger (Lewis Black) and Disgust (Mindy Kaling) attempt to help the struggling girl cope with her new reality. The film explores the idea that every emotional experience and memory, though not always pleasant, has a purpose in bringing us to a greater awareness of and connection to our world.

WHAT GRATITUDE CAN DO FOR YOU

Giving thanks is more than just a polite move: it can transform your mood, outlook and health too

By Louisa Kamps

COUNT YOUR BLESSINGS. SAY "THANK YOU." CONSIDER yourself lucky. These are directives our parents gave us so that we would grow into decent people with decent manners. It turns out that the same advice also helps make our brain and body healthier. "There is a magnetic appeal to gratitude," says Robert Emmons, a professor of psychology at the University of California, Davis, and a pioneer of gratitude research. "It speaks to a need that's deeply entrenched." We need to give thanks and be thanked, just as it's important to feel respected and connected socially. From an evolutionary perspective, feelings of gratitude probably helped bind communities together. When people appreciate the goodness they've received, they feel compelled to give back. This interdependence allows not only an individual but also society as a whole to survive and prosper. It's easy, in these modern times, to forget this, however. We're too busy or distracted, or we've unwittingly become a tad self-entitled. We disconnect from others and suffer consequences such as loneliness, anger—or even a less robust immune system.

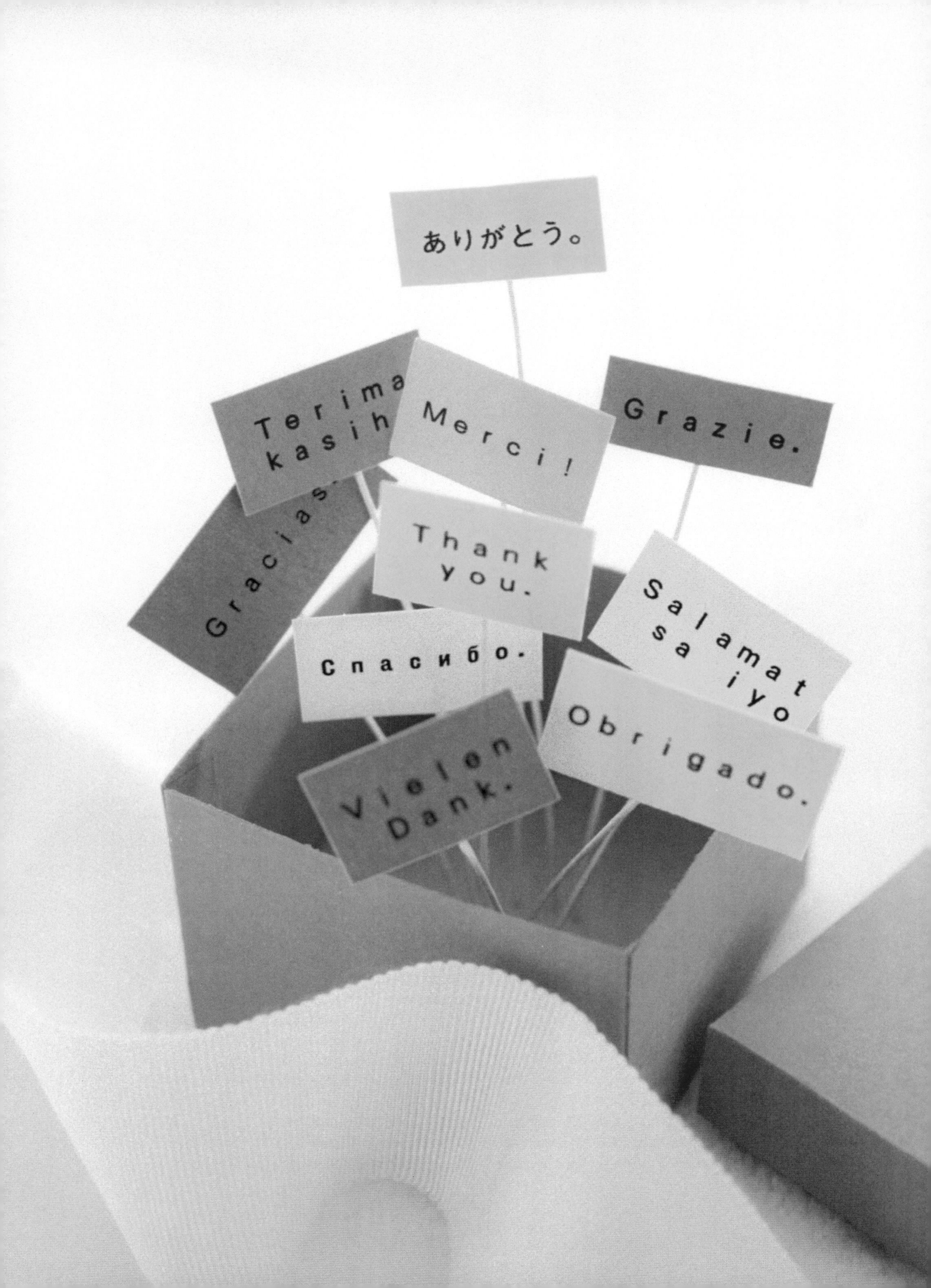

ありがとう。

Terima kasih

Gracias

Merci!

Grazie.

Thank you.

Спасибо.

Salamat sa iyo

Vielen Dank.

Obrigado.

Gratitude can calm down the nervous system and rewire the fight-or-flight stress response, ultimately helping us become more resilient.

"Gratitude serves as a corrective," says Emmons, the author of the book *Gratitude Works!* But by gratitude, he doesn't mean just uttering "Hey, thanks" or shooting off a perfunctory email. He means establishing a full-on gratitude ritual, whether it's a morning meditation of what you're thankful for, a bedtime counting of blessings or a gratitude journal [see "How to Give Thanks" on facing page]. This concerted, consistent effort to notice and appreciate the good things flowing to us—from the crunch of autumn leaves to, yes, the Thanksgiving turkey—changes us for the better on many levels, say gratitude experts. Here's how.

YOU'LL FEEL HAPPIER

In a seminal study by Emmons, subjects who wrote down one thing for which they were grateful every day reported being 25% happier for a full six months after following this practice for just three weeks. In a University of Pennsylvania study, subjects wrote letters of gratitude to people who had done them a major service but had never been fully thanked. After the subjects personally presented these letters, they reported substantially decreased symptoms of depression for as long as a full month.

YOU'LL BOOST YOUR ENERGY LEVELS

In Emmons's gratitude-journal studies, those who regularly wrote down things for which they were thankful consistently reported an ever-increasing sense of vitality. Control subjects who simply kept a general diary saw little increase, if any. The reason is unclear, but improvements in physical health (discussed later), also associated with giving thanks, may have something to do with it. The better your body functions, the more energetic you feel.

YOU'LL GET HEALTHIER

A gratitude practice has also been associated with improved kidney function, reduced blood-pressure and stress-hormone levels and a stronger heart. Experts believe that the link comes from the tendency of grateful people to appreciate their health more than others do, which leads them to take better care of themselves. They avoid deleterious behaviors like smoking and drinking excessive alcohol. They exercise, on average, 33% more and sleep an extra half-hour a night.

YOU'LL BE MORE RESILIENT

When we notice kindness and other gifts that benefit us, our brains become wired to seek out the positives in any situation, even dire ones. As a result, we're better at bouncing back from loss and trauma. "A grateful stance toward life is relatively immune to both fortune and misfortune," says Emmons. We see the blessings, not just the curses.

YOU'LL IMPROVE YOUR RELATIONSHIP

A 2012 *Journal of Personality and Social Psychology* study of more than 300 coupled people found that those who felt more appreciated by their partner were more likely to appreciate their partner in return and to remain in the relationship nine months later, compared with couples who didn't feel appreciated by each other. Christine Carter, a sociologist at the Greater Good Science Center at the University of California, Berkeley, notes that gratitude can rewire our brains to appreciate the things in our relationship that are going well. It can calm down the nervous system and counter the fight-or-flight stress response, she says. You can't be grateful and resentful at the same time.

YOU'LL BE A NICER PERSON

People can't help but pay gratitude forward. When appreciation is expressed, it triggers a biological response in the recipient's brain, including a surge of the feel-good chemical dopamine, says Emmons. So when you express gratitude toward a spouse, a colleague or a friend, he or she feels grateful in return, and the back-and-forth continues. What's more, thanking your benefactors makes them feel good about the kind acts that they've done, so they'll want to continue doing them, not only for you but also for others.

How to Give Thanks

RESEARCH HAS SHOWN THAT ONE OF THE best ways to home in on the people and the experiences we appreciate is through writing in a gratitude journal. Recording our thoughts, by hand or electronically, helps us focus them, says psychologist Robert Emmons, who says that he too does this exercise to remind himself "how good gratitude is. It gives us time to understand better the meaning and importance of people and events in our lives." Here are strategies for maximizing the benefits.

Go for depth rather than breadth

This will help you truly savor what you appreciate and keep your journal from becoming simply a list of nice thoughts. (Journals like that tend to get abandoned.)

Write consistently

But it's OK if you can't do it every day. Once or twice a week is enough to boost happiness.

Write freely

Don't sweat the grammar and spelling. No one else will see this journal unless you want someone to.

Don't think of this as just one more self-improvement project

Rather, it's an opportunity to reflect on other people and the above-and-beyond things that they've done for you, says Emmons. In other words, "it's not all about us," he says. "This may be the most important lesson about trying to become more grateful."

Author and public speaker Mallika Chopra, shown here, teaches people worldwide how to live a more balanced, joyful life.

YES, YOU CAN LIVE WITH INTENT

Finding your purpose can bring new meaning to your days, shares Mallika Chopra in her new book, *Living with Intent*. And the entrepreneur/mom, who is Deepak Chopra's daughter, wants to help you do just that

By Mallika Chopra

HEN I WAS GROWING UP, MY FATHER ENCOURAGED MY brother and me to start every day by consciously thinking about what we wanted. He would ask us a question that still echoes in my mind: What do you want?

Being kids, our responses included things like a new computer game, tickets to the Celtics and a trip to Hawaii. My father would listen patiently and acknowledge our material desires, and then he would gently ask: "How about love? Compassion? Connection? Inspiration? Purpose?"

We were taught at a very young age to ask daily for the qualities in our lives that would make us feel happy, loved, secure, energized and purposeful. And through this process we began each day setting an intention.

What do we mean when we talk about intention? Intents aren't merely goals. They come from the soul, from somewhere deep inside us where we get clarity on our heartfelt desires for happiness, acceptance, health and love. By thinking about our intents, cultivating and expressing them, we create the climate in which they're more likely to happen. But intents also need to be nurtured, to be given time to come to fruition.

The notion of intent goes back millennia. Wisdom traditions from around the world talk about intent as the driving force of creation, and the concept plays a significant role in a number of religious creeds, including Hinduism and Buddhism. Intention in Sanskrit is *samkalpa*, or an idea formed in the mind or heart. "Right intention" is the second element of the Buddha's Noble Eightfold Path, the teachings that describe the way to end personal suffering and achieve enlightenment. Right intention says, essentially: treat yourself and others with kindness and compassion while living in alignment with your deepest values.

In the Buddhist tradition, intention is about living each moment with integrity and in keeping with what matters most to you. Buddhists believe that by carrying your intentions with you moment to moment and trying to live in accord with your deepest values, you are more likely to set wise goals—and do the necessary work to achieve them.

The Hebrew word *kavanah* describes the total awareness and attention you should strive to bring to every moment of your life; it's a way of giving meaning to your actions. For instance, prayer without *kavanah*, or intention, is little more than meaningless words. Even Christian prayer in which you ask God for what you want can be thought of as a form of intention.

More recently, scientists have tried to sort out how—or if—intent works, and most of the research has focused on intercessory prayer. Can praying for people help them heal? The results are mixed. Some studies show a robust effect, some none at all. But in one recent study, investigators at Royal Adelaide Hospital Cancer Centre in Australia looked at whether prayer could improve cancer patients' spiritual and emotional well-being. For six months, a Christian prayer group from a church some distance away prayed for slightly more than half the patients. When compared with the control group, who didn't receive the church's prayers, the prayed-for patients showed small but significant improvements in spiritual and emotional well-being. They had no idea that they were being prayed for, but they improved anyway.

By what mechanism could prayer heal these patients? My father believes that consciousness itself is a fundamental force—as basic as gravity—but one we don't yet have the scientific tools to understand. It could be that conscious intention generates electrostatic or magnetic energy, and the invisible flow has a small but measurable effect on behavior—our own as well as others'. In any case, there's solid evidence for one piece of the puzzle: our thoughts and beliefs can affect our own health.

Just look at the placebo effect, in which a sham treatment produces positive results merely because the patient believes it will. Placebos work almost as well as potent antidepressants in treating mild to moderate depression, and they've been shown to reduce symptoms in Parkinson's, Crohn's disease and multiple sclerosis. Our minds have a powerful influence on our bodies—and our lives. So

Everyday Ways to Be More Present

Below are some things that have helped me as I clear the obstacles from my path

Go for a walk outside
Notice and appreciate how intention plays itself out in the universe—how a flock of birds turns at the same time or how an army of ants marches to its own rhythm. It is powerful just to notice and appreciate what's around you, without feeling pressure to do anything more. For some, writing down free-flowing thoughts or observations in a journal is a great exercise for continued quiet reflection.

Plant a seed in your garden or in a pot on a sunny windowsill in your home
It can be any type of seed—flower, fruit or vegetable. Take responsibility for watering it daily and exposing it to sunlight. Enjoy its beauty and your nurturing power when the seed blossoms into its own unique expression.

Identify a person in your family or community who appears to be living daily with intention
It may be anyone: your mom, the postman or the clerk at the grocery store. Appreciate the important role that person plays in the lives around her or him.

Intent Exercise

"What does the universe want from me?"

> Set aside five minutes to meditate or just sit quietly. Choose a place where you feel happy and secure.
>
> Take a few minutes to settle down, breathing in deeply, inhaling and exhaling comfortably. Not trying to control your breath, not trying to control anything. Just letting it flow and its rhythm relax you.
>
> Ask yourself the following questions. Don't feel the need to answer the questions. Just take time to experience what comes up when you ask.
> *Who am I?*
> Pause for a few seconds, and repeat the question.
> *What do I want?*
> Pause again for a few seconds, and then repeat the question.
> *How can I serve?*
> Pause, then repeat the question.
>
> Take another breath and ask yourself:
> *What does the universe want from me?*
> Do not feel as if you need to have a clear answer to these questions. Just see what percolates in these quiet moments.

INCUBATE: Quiet your mind to tap into your deepest intentions; see where this leads.

NOTICE: Become mindful of your thoughts and actions, and pay attention to what they tell you about what gives you meaning and a sense of purpose—and look for signs that can point you toward your true path.

TRUST: Have confidence in your inner knowing—and in the messages the universe sends you—and allow that knowledge to guide you forward.

EXPRESS: Write down your intentions, say them out loud or share them with others to fully embrace them and help you move ahead in your journey.

NURTURE: Be gentle with yourself as you try to find your way. Intention isn't always a straightforward path, just as life isn't. Giving yourself opportunities to try—and fail—is often part of, and even crucial to, the process.

TAKE ACTION: Once you've identified an intent, or even multiple ones, don't sit and wait for it to magically manifest; instead take the practical steps that can make each become a reality. It may be easiest to choose one intent first and set short-term goals to help you get started.

why not use our minds to improve our lives? Why not set an intention to become a more caring person, to attract love or to contribute to the betterment of humanity?

What would you like to change? What parts of your life aren't working? What's missing? By considering these questions, you can uncover the seeds of your deepest longings. What small changes can you make to feel more rested, happier, more connected, more inspired? Embracing small personal changes can be the first step toward creating greater change in the world, and humanity at large.

While I fully believe that intention is a powerful tool for personal change, I also know that putting the concept into practice can feel confusing. Is there a way to describe the process that would make it clearer and simpler? As I'm trying to sort out the issue, my practical, analytical left brain kicks into gear. Eventually I hit upon six strategies that can help us all find our way forward, INTENT: Incubate, Notice, Trust, Express, Nurture and Take Action.

Why take the trouble to try to live with intention? Why not just drift along without making the effort to clarify what you want? Years ago, David Sable, the CEO of Young & Rubicam (now Y&R), told me this Hasidic tale that gets at the heart of why I believe so deeply in making an effort to live with intent:

The great Rabbi Zusya was lying on his deathbed, tears streaming down his face. When his followers asked him why he was crying, he said, "If God asks me why I wasn't like Moses, I'll say I wasn't blessed with that kind of leadership ability or wisdom. But if God asks me, 'Zusya, why weren't you Zusya? Why didn't you fulfill your own highest potential? Why didn't you find your inner self?' What will I say then?"

I want to live my life to its fullest potential. I want to embrace my own purpose, however large or small it may be. Where would you like to go? What's calling to you?

Adapted from *Living with Intent: My Somewhat Messy Journey to Purpose, Peace and Joy.* © 2015 by Mallika Chopra. Published by Harmony Books, an imprint of Penguin Random House LLC.

THE FAITH FACTOR

To understand the modern mindfulness movement, take this crash course in world religions

By Andréa Ford

T HERE IS NOTHING NECESSARILY RELIGIOUS ABOUT MIND-fulness. You don't have to follow a deity or dogma to focus your attention on your body and mind. But being contemplative plays a role in most of the leading religions. "We see the traces of meditative consciousness throughout almost all faith traditions," says Jeff Wilson, a professor of religious studies and East Asian studies at the University of Waterloo in Ontario and the author of *Mindful America: The Mutual Transformation of Buddhist Meditation and American Culture.* Today's mindfulness revolution, with its earliest roots in Buddhism, has caused people of all faiths to "reexamine their own traditions, looking for parallel types of practices, or to import Buddhist-originated mindfulness and domesticate it, so it becomes Jewish or Christian or Muslim," he says.

BUDDHISM

Sometime between the 6th and 4th centuries B.C. in northeastern India, the prince Siddhartha wandered beyond his palace and discovered rampant anguish. Disheartened, he left his home and sat under a fig tree, resolving to meditate until he discovered a solution to suffering. After a long period, he became the enlightened Buddha. The traditions that sprang up

Monks of the Wushu Training Center in Henan Province, China, practice meditation as a means to enlightenment.

Some Sufis, adherents of a mystical branch of Islam, are famous for the practice of whirling, a meditative dancing ritual believed to promote unity with God.

around this story are the inspiration for the way mindfulness is practiced today.

Meditation was originally practiced primarily by monks. But between the 18th and 20th centuries, when southeast Asia was being colonized by Christians, the lay public was encouraged to participate in an effort to preserve the Buddhist faith. "That was the beginning of mindfulness for the masses," Wilson says.

Today, Buddhists worldwide continue to meditate daily, often in the morning. Most important, modern Buddhists attempt to carry that mind-set throughout their day, in the way they eat, work and interact with others. Some of the common tools of mindfulness come from Buddhists, who meditate and use *tingsha* (hand cymbals) or singing bowls.

HINDUISM

Hinduism encompasses a very large and diverse collection of traditions. While these groups don't share the exact same deities and philosophies, meditation is the common thread.

Even before the advent of Buddhism, the Sanskrit collection of sacred Hindu texts known as the Vedas was being written between 1500 and 500 B.C. These writings contain some of the world's oldest records of mantras, yoga and meditation, which, Hinduism teaches, is the way to achieve a state of pure self-awareness.

JUDAISM

A central practice of Judaism is the observance of Shabbat—the commandment of resting for one day each week. Like mindfulness, the ritual is a restorative exercise.

Mindfulness has long been part of Judaism—with links to the ancient scholars of the faith—but the tradition had fallen out of favor by the 1970s, as mystical practices were considered too difficult for the average person, says Torah life coach and writer Frumma Rosenberg-Gottlieb. That changed in the late 1970s, when Jewish leaders tried to incorporate a "kosher," user-friendly version of mindfulness. Rosenberg-Gottlieb says the connection was not hard to make. "In scripture, we see all these allusions to the great Jewish leaders being shepherds. Why? Because they were able to sit contemplatively in the fields and be mindful," she says.

> **Modern Buddhists attempt to carry mindfulness throughout their day as they eat, work and interact with others.**

Today, certain sects, following ancient tradition, practice an informal period of mindfulness outside before even entering the synagogue to pray. Some Jews use the Hebrew equivalent of mantras, repeating words like *echad* (one) in place of *om*. Others use a *shiviti*, an illustration used for visualization, contemplation and meditation.

CHRISTIANITY

Contemplation—a foundation of Christian mysticism—is a great example of a mindful practice, says Wilson. Although its purpose is more about focusing one's attention to achieve unity with God than to promote wellness, it resembles modern mindfulness in its emphasis on concentration. Historically a monastic practice, contemplation is increasingly becoming part of modern lay life, through popular initiatives such as the Center for Action and Contemplation in Albuquerque, N.M., an institution founded by Franciscan friar and best-selling author Father Richard Rohr in the 1980s that offers daily meditations and online courses.

Many other Christian rituals require intense focus. Roman Catholics use the rosary as a tool to aid in concentration. The beads aid individuals or groups in reciting prayers while focusing on "mysteries," or moments of Jesus's life. Another practice, called adoration, involves solemnly meditating on the Eucharist, the Christian sacrament of bread and wine.

Group singing, a common element of Christian (and other religious) worship, may offer some of the same brain benefits as mindfulness, including relief from stress and depression. A 2013 study in *Frontiers in Psychology* suggested that group hymn singing—essentially a form of guided breath—may sync up the heart rates of participants.

Less ancient varieties of Christianity emphasize focusing on the present as well. For Quakers, stillness and silence are a core aspect of worship. Quaker Friends use the term "centering down" to describe quieting the mind at the opening of a meeting. As Quaker pastor Philip Gulley explains it in his book *Living the Quaker Way*, "True centering down transcends worship. It is to bring one's entire life into a place of listening and learning."

ISLAM

Mindfulness is so central to Islam that the originator of the faith was in fact in a state of meditation at the outset of his ministry. In A.D. 610, a 40-year-old Muhammad was spending time alone in a cave near Mecca, concerned about injustices in society. One night, as he meditated, the angel Gabriel appeared, giving the prophet his first revelation.

Meditation remains a big part of Muslim life. Five times each day, adherents perform *salat*, a worship ritual involving a series of postures. Some Muslims liken the physical sequence of standing, raising arms, bending, lying prostrate and kneeling to something like yoga. In fact, a 2014 study by researchers from Al-Quds University in Jerusalem and the University of Malaya in Kuala Lumpur, published in the *Journal of Alternative and Complementary Medicine*, found that practicing *salat* regularly may decrease anxiety and cardiovascular risk—benefits also seen with yoga. Whirling is another form of mindful movement; it is practiced by dervishes in the Sufi tradition of Islam, who believe the ritual brings them closer to God.

POWER A.M. ROUTINES, TESTED

In search of less-harried days, our writer tried the morning rituals of Michelle Obama, Mark Zuckerberg and other high achievers. Did it clear his mind—or make him lose it?

By Dan Bova

VER HAVE ONE OF THOSE MORN-ings when everything just falls into place and you glide into work on a flying carpet of seren-ity? Yeah, neither have I.

If your mornings are anything like my fam-ily's, you start each day in a nuclear bomb of madness, a whirlwind of crazy. You are in a daily desperate fight to get everyone dressed, fed and out the door with their shoes on the right feet and minimal tears on their cheeks. And that's just the adults.

I don't want my mornings to leave my brain scrambled and my throat feeling as if I just sat through a Knicks game shouting "You stink!" from the nosebleed seats. I prefer to be like all of these successful people you read about who swear by super-early routines that keep them calm, relaxed and on the path to making more money than God and Mr. Monopoly combined. So recently I began setting my alarm for 5 a.m., hop-ing to get a taste of all that good stuff. I can't say that reaching over to hit the snooze but-ton and knocking over a full glass of water on the nightstand was the most tranquil way to start my day, but it did get me out of bed.

> **Many billionaires say the first thing they do each day is meditate and seek answers to the big questions in life.**

Many billionaires say the first thing they do each day is meditate and seek answers to the big questions in life. I tried this one morn-ing. The biggest question that popped into my mind was "Why am I awake right now?" Then came peace, as I instantly fell back asleep.

THE DREAM: A CALM KICK START

I read that Sir Richard Branson leaves the blinds in his bedroom up so that the rising sun can serve as his alarm clock. (That's how rich this guy is: he uses a medium-size star instead of an iPhone ringtone.) Next Sir Richard hits the beach of his private island for some pre-breakfast kiteboarding. I wanted to try this, but I don't live on a private island and the nearest body of water is in my basement if it rained a lot the previous night.

In an interview with Oprah, First Lady Mi-chelle Obama explained that she needs to exer-cise in the morning or else she gets depressed. I don't have a home gym, but consulting my personal physician, Dr. Googlesearch, I've learned that a person burns approximately five calories going up and down a flight of stairs. So taking into account the number of times I go back upstairs because I left my phone—oh wait, my wallet, and, damn, the keys are in yesterday's jeans!—I burn approx-imately 37,000 calories every morning. Not sure it cures my morning blues, though.

Facebook's boy billionaire Mark Zucker-berg is famous for having a clothes closet filled with multiple sets of the same exact outfit. He says he does this to avoid clutter-ing his thoughts about Facebook with deci-sions about what he'll wear on any given day. He finds this freeing. I find it ridiculous. How much brainpow-er does a male person expend picking out his outfit for the day? "Today I will wear a shirt and pants." Not only is this easy, it is probably the only good decision I will make all day. Why should I take that tiny victory away from myself?

Huffington Post founder Arianna Huffing-ton recently wrote an entire book about sleep-ing. In it, she says that sleep deprivation is "the new smoking." She heartily recommends that we get a solid eight hours of sleep ev-ery night. To accomplish this, I climbed into bed at 9:00 sharp, leaving my kids to tuck my wife, Lisa, in after she passed out on the couch binge-watching *The Americans.*

THE REALITY: A MAD SCRAMBLE

Lisa and I used to pray to any and all gods that our children would let us sleep in, but now as they get older, most school-day mornings we can be heard gently whispering in their ears, "IT'S 7:15! GET UP!"

When they do flop out of bed, it is an unre-lenting race to get them fed and dressed, pack

Daily habits of the rich and famous include, clockwise from bottom left: Richard Branson kiteboards before breakfast; Arianna Huffington aims for eight hours of sleep nightly; Michelle Obama works out; Mark Zuckerberg's gray T-shirt uniform takes the guesswork out of dressing.

their lunches, print out whatever homework they forgot to print the night before, and call our neighbor Mary to ask if we can use her printer because ours is out of toner.

Most mornings, Lisa and I somehow manage to tag-team this eye-crusted wrestling match successfully. And then some mornings, not so much. Like when our son Henry was in third grade and my wife got a call from the school principal. "Henry is OK," she was assured, but there was "an incident" at lunch and the school was "investigating." While eat-

ing his snack bag of grated mozzarella cheese (yes, that's weird, but that's not the weird part), Henry found tiny metal screws mixed in with his munchies. The principal explained that the students were being questioned to find out what awful person could have done such a thing. Lisa called and told me the story, and like in some movie in which the hero cop has all these flashbacks and realizes that *he* actually murdered all of those people, my brain snapped everything together. The night before, I took the air conditioner out of the

Finding a helpful routine is highly personal; what some people find most effective may not work at all for others.

dining room window, put the screws in a baggie and left the baggie on the counter. That morning, Lisa was cleaning and—missing the fact that it had screws in it—put the seemingly empty baggie back in the baggie box. Minutes later, while making Henry's lunch, I took the very same baggie out of the box—also missing the fact that it had screws in it—and filled it with shredded cheese. So, in effect, I was the awful person who would put screws in a child's lunch. Imagine us trying to explain that to the principal on a follow-up call.

ENLIGHTENMENT ISN'T ONE-SIZE-FITS-ALL

Despite my best efforts to wake with enough time to not accidentally feed my children hardware supplies, I've given up on the millionaire morning routine. One man's 6 a.m. mindfulness is another man's torture. Turns out that getting up crazy early makes me crazy tired. Don't get me wrong; I love falling so deeply asleep on the train that I wake up screaming "Where am I?" But the problem is,

if I'm in a meeting and someone's phone goes off with the same ringtone as my alarm, I beg to sleep for five more minutes.

I asked Jeremy Bloom, a two-time Olympic skier, former NFL player and the author of *Fueled by Failure: Using Detours and Defeats to Power Progress*, what went wrong with my experiment. In short: kind of the whole thing. "Copying someone else's routine is not a good idea, since what works for one person may not work very well for another," he says. "You have to understand who *you* are." The point isn't *when* these power players take a moment for mindful reflection; it's that they do it in a way that works for them.

Since my conversation with Bloom, I've realized that just making a habit of riding my bike to and from my commuter train puts me in a better frame of mind. But it's really late at night, after everyone else is asleep, that I find my true chance to clear my mind. It has yet to bring me billions, but it has allowed me to clear an amazing number of levels on *Halo*, and that, it turns out, is all the reward I need.

Get Your Mornings Under Control Like a Navy SEAL

Brandon Webb

TO MAKE IT OUT THE DOOR, MOST PARENTS have to navigate a minefield. (Missing backpacks! Unsigned permission slips! Oops, coffee stain on work clothes!) A former Navy SEAL sniper and the CEO of Force12 Media, Brandon Webb wants to help you conquer the a.m. insanity. Here is his action plan:

FOCUS ON A SINGLE TARGET

The military teaches you that when your plan is falling apart, you need to immediately prioritize your problems. So, say you have to get your kids to school and make it to a work meeting, and the plumber is running late. What is the most vitally important thing you need to take care of? I'd say the first thing you need to do is get the kids to school. Concentrate on that; don't even think about anything else. Once you get them off your plate, you can refocus on the next task. It's like the old saying: How do you eat an elephant? One bite at a time.

TROUBLESHOOT

I always think about what can go wrong and have a contingency plan. That's why if I have something important to get up for, I set two alarms. You never know when the power is going to go out. Plan for the worst.

PREP AND THEN PREP SOME MORE

Developing a habit of taking a little bit of time at night to prep for the morning will make all the difference. If you know your routine is going to be messed up—Mom has an early doctor's appointment, for example—then Dad better get his stuff together the night before to make sure he doesn't have a mess on his hands when the clock is ticking in the morning. When I had a mission, I was always packed and ready to go—that way, when you get up in the morning, you don't have to think.

PRETEND YOU'RE JUMPING OUT OF A PLANE

There can be a lot of distractions in the morning, so you have to train yourself to block them out. When I went to military free-fall school, I was packing my parachutes for a timed exercise, and these guys came over and started screaming at me to hurry up. I didn't even look at them. I just took my time and did what I knew I had to do. Block out the noise, complete the task at hand and move on to the next one. Otherwise, you get rattled and distracted, and that's going to be a big problem when you jump out of the plane.

REMEMBER TO BREATHE

You can only control and plan for so much. Sometimes things just go badly. When that happens, you have to take time to stop and take a couple of deep breaths; this will hit an internal reset button. Then it's back to: What is the one thing I have to do right now? Not the eight other things I have stacked up in my crazy day—what is right in front of my face that I need to deal with? Complete that task and then go on to the next one and the next one and the next one.

PART THREE

Eat, Play, Thrive

THE COMPLETE GUIDE TO YOGA

This ancient practice has powerful health and mood benefits, according to mounting science. Here is how to find the ideal type for you, prevent injury—and slip in a routine when you can't get to class

By Holly Pevzner

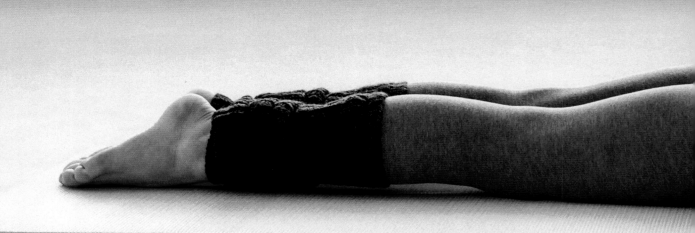

FINDING A YOGA CLASS USED TO be simple. You'd walk into your local gym, and there would be the class. Your choices were few because, well, there weren't that many people looking to get their *om* on: in 2001, 4.3 million Americans were hitting the yoga mat; by 2016, that number had jumped almost ninefold, to more than 36 million. Studios, gyms and rec centers now offer an estimated 800-plus styles to choose from, says Leigh Crews, a spokesperson with the American Council on Exercise. Some of this has to do with yoga's (well-deserved) reputation for being an excellent stress reliever. But a big part of yoga's popularity surge is that it's just plain good exercise. Virtually any type of yoga improves strength, flexibility and balance, explains John P. Porcari, the director of the clinical exercise physiology program at the University of Wisconsin–La Crosse. "The more intense styles can also help you shape up and trim down."

Want to take full advantage of that powerful collection of benefits? Read on for everything you need to know, whether you are a first-timer or a regular looking to take your poses to a whole new level.

If you are JUST BEGINNING or want the best MIND-BODY COMBO, try HATHA

Poses are straightforward, and the pace is unhurried. "You do a pose, come out of it, then do another," explains Mark Stephens, the author of *Teaching Yoga: Essential Foundations and Techniques.* "It's an excellent style for beginners." Props such as blocks and bolsters are often used to help you get the right alignment. But it's not just about the body; your teacher will also encourage you to focus on breathing, relaxation and meditation (which may involve chanting). And all of this mindfulness has a real-world benefit: a study in the journal *Psychosomatic Medicine* found that women who practice hatha yoga once or twice a week recover from stress faster than those who don't.

If you want to GET SLIM, try ASHTANGA or POWER YOGA

These two styles provide all the regular benefits of yoga with the fat-blasting bonus of a killer cardio session. Both focus on flowing from one pose to the next without rest—making for a terrific calorie burn (about 500 per hour). "The practice is meant to generate heat in your body," says Mandy Ingber, the yoga instructor behind Jennifer Aniston's ageless body. So, yes, you will sweat. A lot.

In ashtanga, the more traditional of the two, you'll begin with chanting and then follow a sequence of poses ("asanas") that never changes. In a power-yoga class, the poses vary each time and there's usually none of the spiritual aspect.

A large study in the journal *Alternative Therapies in Health and Medicine* confirms that women get lean in these classes: practicing yoga of any kind at least once a week for four years or more staves off middle-age spread.

If you want to CHILL OUT, try YIN YOGA

Named for the calm half of yin-and-yang, this style requires you to move slowly into poses (most of them performed while seated or ly-

What About Hot Yoga?

In Bikram, a.k.a. "hot yoga," you practice in a steamy 105° room. It isn't for everyone. "The heat and postures—which are the same each time—build strength and get you into a deeper stretch," says instructor Mandy Ingber. This is a good thing if you're looking to blast calories (as many as 500 per hour) and get limber, but it's uncomfortable if you're heat-averse—and downright dangerous if you are pregnant or have heart issues.

Pain-Free Posing

AS MORE OF US TWIST INTO poses, injuries are on the rise: in a 2009 study, 39% of yoga teachers, yoga therapists and doctors reported seeing more injuries than before. And yoga-related visits to emergency rooms are also increasing. Here's how to stay off the sidelines.

TAKE IT EASY

"A lot of yoga injuries are from trying too hard," says yoga author Timothy McCall. Holding your breath, panting—they're signs you're pushing too far.

DON'T GO TO EXTREMES

Poses such as headstands can potentially put too much weight on your cervical spine, upping your risk of injury. "These should not be done by anyone who hasn't had a lot of yoga experience," cautions Mike McArdle, the New York yoga instructor behind Bethenny Frankel's *Skinnygirl Workout* DVD.

STOP IF YOU FEEL PAIN

It's OK to challenge your muscles, but "if you feel a sharp or electric-type pain, back off," advises physician Sara Gottfried.

ing down) and then stay in them for up to five minutes to allow for a deeper stretch and time to just, well, be.

Not surprisingly, yin yoga is particularly good at activating the part of your nervous system that helps you bounce back from pain and stress, says Sara Gottfried, an integrative physician in Berkeley, Calif., and the author of the book *The Hormone Cure*. Expect meditative music and lots of attention to breathing, as well as those centers of spiritual energy known as chakras—all elements that add to the serene allure of the practice.

If you're PRONE TO ACHES, try IYENGAR

As with many types of yoga, the poses you'll do in an Iyengar class are traditional. The difference is in how those poses are done. Iyengar teachers are trained in biomechanics, so they understand which positions are most likely to cause injuries—and how to modify them by tweaking your form and showing you how to use props to make them less intense, says Stephens. Plus, pausing between poses (as opposed to flowing from one to the next) allows you to perfect your position, so you're less likely to strain something.

Iyengar may even help you recover from injury. A study in the *Archives of Internal Medicine* found that a similar style of yoga, Viniyoga, worked wonders on chronic lower-back pain in just 12 weeks.

FIND THE RIGHT CLASS

The truth is, you can discover a great instructor or class in a church basement, or a questionable one in a fancy yoga studio. Just keep in mind that your teacher should be properly trained, with at least a 200-hour certification from Yoga Alliance, the main yoga education organization in the U.S. Below, the scoop on your options:

Yoga Studio

• **The coaching:**
Most require teachers to have Yoga Alliance certification. Some also require additional in-house training so that teachers can learn the studio's specific style.

• **The classes:**
Practice rooms are Zen-like, and class options abound. Studios that are part of national chains might offer lockers and showers.

• **The crowd:**
Morning classes tend to be smaller (10 to 20 people), but postwork classes can be packed.

Flex in Five

Treat your body to this stretch-you-all-over mini-routine from yoga instructor and DVD star Seane Corn, who teaches around the world. Hold each pose for three to eight breaths

TRIANGLE

Stretches hamstrings and muscles; supports the spine; boosts mobility in shoulders

· Stand with feet five feet apart; turn left foot out, right foot slightly in. Inhale; raise arms parallel to floor. Exhale; hinge at left hip; rotate so that left torso comes down over left leg; rest left hand on lower leg and reach right hand straight up from shoulder. Hold; return to start; repeat on other side.

WIDE-LEG STANDING TWIST

Stretches hamstrings; increases spine flexibility; improves mobility in shoulders

· Stand with feet a bit closer, feet parallel. With spine long, exhale; fold forward from hips; bring hands to floor; hold. Inhale, twist torso left; reach left hand straight up; hold. Exhale; return to center; inhale; repeat on right. Exhale; return to center; inhale; return to standing.

LOCUST

Increases spine flexibility; strengthens back muscles; opens shoulders; stimulates central nervous system

· Lie facedown with forehead on floor, legs straight, arms by sides, palms up. Inhale, lifting head, upper body, arms and legs off floor; stretch legs and arms back, keeping gaze on floor. Hold and then slowly lower back down.

FOLDED FORWARD BEND

Calms nervous system; stretches hamstrings and back muscles

· Sit on the edge of a folded blanket, legs straight and together in front of you, arms by sides. Keeping spine long, exhale and fold forward over legs, stretching arms forward to hold sides of feet or calves; hold and then inhale and slowly lift back up to sitting.

Namaste Through the Ages

From ancient practice to Instagram hashtag, yoga is always having a moment

BY LINDSEY MURRAY

Start here!

3300–1900 B.C.: YOGA IS DEVELOPED BY THE INDUS-SARASVATI CIVILIZATION IN NORTHERN INDIA

1947: RUSSIAN ACTRESS INDRA DEVI BRINGS YOGA TO HOLLYWOOD, TEACHING SUCH A-LISTERS AS GRETA GARBO, EVA GABOR AND GLORIA SWANSON AT HER EPONYMOUS STUDIO.

1956: B.K.S. IYENGAR TRAVELS FROM INDIA TO NEW YORK AND FINDS ALMOST NO INTEREST IN YOGA. A DECADE LATER, HE WRITES *LIGHT ON YOGA*, A SEMINAL BOOK THAT HELPS FUEL THE MOVEMENT IN THE WEST.

1969: SWAMI SATCHIDANANDA KICKS OFF THE WOODSTOCK FESTIVAL WITH GOOD VIBES, URGING THE CROWD OF 500,000 TO "LET ALL OUR ACTIONS, AND ALL OUR ARTS, EXPRESS YOGA."

1998: MADONNA'S ALBUM *RAY OF LIGHT* INCLUDES SEVERAL SANSKRIT CHANTS AND A SONG CALLED "SHANTI/ASHTANGI." IT WINS THREE GRAMMYS AND SELLS 4 MILLION COPIES.

1994: ACTRESS–TURNED–FITNESS-STAR JANE FONDA JUMPS ON THE '90S YOGA TRAIN AND RELEASES A BEGINNERS' YOGA VIDEO.

2000: THE YOGA LIFESTYLE BRAND LULULEMON OPENS ITS FIRST STAND-ALONE STORE IN VANCOUVER, KICKING OFF THE "ATHLEISURE" RETAIL CRAZE. (THIRTEEN YEARS LATER, THE COMPANY MAKES HEADLINES FOR ITS UNINTENTIONALLY SEE-THROUGH PANTS.)

2007: GWYNETH PALTROW SHOWS OFF THE PRIVATE YOGA STUDIO INSIDE HER HAMPTONS HOME IN *HOUSE & GARDEN*, CAUSING YOGA LOVERS TO FEEL AN UN-ZEN EMOTION: ENVY.

2010: PINK WOWS WITH HER AERIAL YOGA SKILLS IN A CIRQUE DU SOLEIL–INSPIRED ROUTINE OF "GLITTER IN THE AIR" AT THE 52ND ANNUAL GRAMMY AWARDS.

2009: BASKETBALL GREAT SHAQUILLE O'NEAL UNROLLS HIS MAT IN A CLEVELAND STUDIO, OFFICIALLY MAKING "BROGA" A THING.

2009: FIRST LADY MICHELLE OBAMA ADDS DOWNWARD DOGGING TO THE ANNUAL WHITE HOUSE EASTER EGG ROLL.

2011: MANDY INGBER— BEST KNOWN AS JENNIFER ANISTON'S YOGA TRAINER— RELEASES HER *YOGALOSOPHY* SERIES ON DVD.

2013: IN RESPONSE TO OVERWHELMING DEMAND FROM PLAYERS, THE SEATTLE SEAHAWKS MAKE YOGA A MANDATORY PART OF TEAM WORKOUTS.

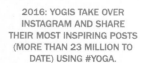

2016: YOGIS TAKE OVER INSTAGRAM AND SHARE THEIR MOST INSPIRING POSTS (MORE THAN 23 MILLION TO DATE) USING #YOGA.

2014: THE U.N. DECLARES JUNE 21 AS INTERNATIONAL DAY OF YOGA, PRAISING THE PRACTICE FOR ENCOURAGING PEACE AND STRESS RELIEF.

"In big classes, there's usually additional help from yoga instructors who are being mentored by the main teacher," says Kay Kay Clivio, the head of teacher training at Pure Yoga.

• **The cost:**
$12 to $20 per class; $100 to $190 per month for unlimited classes. Ask about free trial classes.

The Gym

• **The coaching:**
Teachers are usually certified by Yoga Alliance, but since many gyms don't pay well, you may end up with a teacher who's certified but less experienced, says Timothy McCall, the author of *Yoga as Medicine*.

• **The classes:**
Most gyms provide props and a variety of classes, including yoga hybrids (though the benefits of pure yoga often get lost); the atmosphere is less serene than a studio's. Then again, you get to hit the steam room after class.

• **The crowd:**
After-work classes average 25 to 40 people—usually without additional teaching help—and classmates may be less serious about yoga.

• **The cost:**
Usually free with gym membership.

The Rec Center

• **The coaching:**
Teachers sometimes have group-fitness (as opposed to yoga-specific) certification, which is not ideal.

• **The classes:**
Usually just a few styles; BYO props.

• **The crowd:**
Classes tend to be crowded.

• **The cost:**
Many charge by the class, others by the year. Discounts are often available for residents.

In the end, what matters is that you're comfortable in the class. If your first one isn't a good fit, try a different style, a different teacher or both. And once you find that perfect combination, stick with it, says McCall: "You'll get the most benefits from yoga if you're a regular."

The One Essential

Your own mat, to avoid picking up germs from the shared ones. No need to spring for anything fancy. Just look for one that's grippy so that you don't go sliding into splits every time you strike a pose. Got knee issues? Buy a mat that's 1/4-inch thick (instead of the standard 1/8 inch).

Men Getting Bendy

Guys are discovering yoga in record numbers—and research says that's a very good thing

BY MANDY OAKLANDER

IF THE SOUND OF *OM* IN YOUR YOGA CLASS SEEMS TO HAVE DROPPED AN OCTAVE, IT'S NOT your imagination. From Hollywood brass and NFL linebackers to regular joes looking to get fit, men are turning to the ancient practice to build muscle, improve balance and flexibility and get the benefit yoga is probably best known for: stress relief. "We have definitely seen an increase in men in our classes over the past year," says Jen Zweibel, a manager at the Equinox-owned chain Pure Yoga, where a third of the students in some classes are male. A 2016 poll estimates that men make up 28% of the 36 million Americans who practice yoga, and a handful of recent studies on male yogis suggest that all those downward dogs are worth it.

MORE SATISFACTION

Men who practiced yoga had a better body image than those who worked out in a gym, a recent study found. Yoga also improved their sex life, with men reporting more desire, control and stamina in a study in the *Journal of Sexual Medicine*.

REDUCED STRESS

Yoga's reputation for being relaxing is well established, and a host of recent research on active-duty soldiers backs it up. Researchers found that regular yoga reduced stress, anxiety and depression while improving memory.

LESS ANXIETY

When Vietnam vets practiced yoga, their symptoms of PTSD lessened, according to a study in the *Journal of Traumatic Stress Disorders and Treatment*. A paper that examined police cadets found that taking just six yoga classes reduced tension and anger.

IMPROVED BALANCE

Preventing falls and injury requires good balance. And five months of regular yoga gave men substantially better posture and balance, a 2014 study in the *International Journal of Yoga* found.

A HEALTHIER HEART

Daily yoga was linked to lower blood pressure and cholesterol in older men, according to a study in the journal *Age*. Hypertension and high cholesterol are both major risk factors for heart disease, the U.S.'s No. 1 killer.

INSOMNIA RELIEF

A study in the *Journal of Clinical and Diagnostic Research* found that after eight weeks of yoga, 40 males with insomnia (which can increase stress) were significantly less stressed and more self-confident. Other research suggests that regular yoga might improve sleep quality and duration.

Sources: *Yoga Journal; Consciousness and Cognition; Psychological Reports; Perceptual & Motor Skills; International Journal of Yoga Therapy*

CAN YOU SHED POUNDS ON A MINDFULNESS DIET?

Focusing your senses on a few raisins may sound odd, but mindful eating exercises like this one are leading to weight-loss success

By Kathleen Mulpeter

 HETHER IT'S A CHOCOLATE BAR, A BAG OF CHIPS OR A PINT of rocky road ice cream, most of us have that one food we automatically crave when we're stressed. For Ruth Wolever, an associate professor of physical medicine and rehabilitation at Vanderbilt University Medical Center, the food she longed for when tense was always chocolate-chip cookie dough. So synonymous with stress were these cookie-dough binges that Wolever's friends and family would ask if something was wrong whenever they'd see her reach for it.

Wolever, who is a co-author of *The Mindful Diet: How to Transform Your Relationship with Food for Lasting Weight Loss and Vibrant Health*, was motivated to research eating behaviors after noticing just how much cookie dough she could unintentionally consume. "I'd get so focused on eating it," she says. "It was often outside of my own awareness."

Most people can probably relate to this habit, and not just in times of

Research has shown that a food diary that incorporates mindful details about meals may assist people with their weight loss.

stress. We may find ourselves mindlessly munching when we're bored, when we're watching TV or when we're eating out and dessert arrives that we don't have room for but pick at anyway.

The good news: it's possible to train ourselves to become more conscious of every bite through a practice known as mindful eating. Research suggests this strategy could vastly improve our relationship with food by reducing stress-related overeating—perhaps preventing weight gain in the process.

Mindful eating requires a change in the way you think about food. Instead of automatically finishing everything on your plate, you learn to pay attention to what your body needs—and what it doesn't. Meditation, yoga and breathing exercises are often used to help strengthen these "mindful" muscles. In one recent study published in the *Journal of Consumer Research*, people who completed a meditation exercise before eating chocolate snacks consumed fewer calories over time. Although the meditation group initially ate similar amounts of food as the non-meditation group, they adjusted their caloric intake in future meals, eating less to justify the earlier indulgence. This implies

that mindfulness can help us become more aware of what we take in and better equipped to balance out a dietary splurge with a save.

A LESS PUNISHING TACTIC

"[Mindful eating] allows people to enjoy a relaxed relationship with food—one that doesn't require a constant struggle between willpower and temptation," says Sandra Aamodt, a neuroscientist and the author of *Why Diets Make Us Fat*.

Aamodt emphasizes that this more evolved way of fueling up isn't a magic weight-loss solution. You're not guaranteed to instantly drop three sizes. But by promoting self-compassion, the practice may inhibit stress eating and the weight struggles that often go with it.

Aamodt has experienced this change firsthand. After 30 years as a self-described "yo-yo dieter," she finally made the decision to stop obsessing over her weight. Instead of following a strict diet, she committed to regular exercise and mindful eating habits—and she has maintained a stable weight ever since. Now she enjoys food more and worries about it less.

So why does mindful eating work? According to experts, whereas traditional diets approach weight loss through a set of rules (eat this, don't eat that), mindful eating forces you to rely on internal cues. "Most diets train us to pay attention to externals," says Wolever. "What we should be doing is listening to our bodies: Are we hungry or are we full? Do we need food or something else?"

These sound like obvious questions. But it's no easy feat to simply stop eating the way you're accustomed to, explains Jennifer Daubenmier, an assistant professor at the Osher Center for Integrative Medicine at the University of California, San Francisco.

On a basic level, dieters understand what they should and should not eat, she says. But actually following through often requires a skill set they haven't yet mastered.

"It's really easy to eat for pleasure rather than for hunger," says Daubenmier. "I think many diet programs fail because people don't know how to stop eating this way."

Becoming better attuned to your body's signals may weaken this eating-for-fun instinct; research has linked mindfulness to reduced binge eating, less emotional eating and decreased body weight.

WEIGHT LOSS AND HEALTH GAINS

It also seems to support long-term health. In a study published in the journal *Obesity* in March 2016, Daubenmier and her colleagues observed a connection between mindfulness and lasting physiological benefits. The nearly 200 obese adults in their study were all asked to follow the same diet and exercise regimen. Half the group was given additional information on nutrition and exercise, while the other half was taught mindful eating techniques, as well as yoga, meditation and breathing exercises. To learn to eat mindfully, participants were instructed to eat one raisin. Afterward, the researchers asked them to reflect on it: Did the raisin make them feel full? On a scale of 1 to 10, how full did they feel? What signs of fullness was their body giving them? Gradu-

ally, this exercise was repeated with more-tempting foods.

At the end of the study, both groups lost comparable amounts of weight. But six months later, the mindfulness group had healthier levels of "good" HDL cholesterol and lower levels of triglyceride (a type of blood fat that can increase the risk of clogged arteries and heart disease). One year after the study, they also had lower blood-sugar levels. This suggests that mindfulness may trump traditional dieting when it comes to establishing long-term healthy habits you can stick with.

> By promoting self-compassion, mindful eating may inhibit stress-related bingeing.

Having to think so hard about food may sound a little odd, if not impractical. Many of us frequently eat meals on the go or in small windows of time. But this mode of dining can eventually become second nature, insists Michael Mantzios, a lecturer in health psychology at Birmingham City University in England. He's seen it himself in his research: in a study published in *Psychology & Health* that he co-authored, participants appeared to internalize the message of mindful eating and apply it subconsciously over time. They were divided into two groups; half practiced meditation and half logged their meals in a food diary. The diary group was given a list of mindful questions to answer as they ate, such as "How does this meal taste?" and "How kind are you to yourself now that you ate this meal?"

To Mantzios's surprise, the food-diary group maintained their weight loss even more successfully than the meditation group—and many of the food-diary participants weren't even writing down their answers.

"Some were keeping the diary open to remind themselves of how they should approach their meal," he says. In other words, once they understood how to eat mindfully, the journal's mere existence was enough to prompt them to consider their food in a more thoughtful way.

"If you keep practicing [mindful eating], you'll get to the point where it becomes habitual," says Mantzios. "In other words, you will become mindlessly very mindful."

FOURTEEN WAYS TO EAT IN THE MOMENT (AND LOVE IT)

Simple strategies for connecting with your hunger and avoiding stress snacking

By Ellen Seidman

C HANCES ARE, YOU VERY RECENTLY THOUGHT ABOUT EAT-
ing or soon will: people make some 200 decisions a day
about food and drink, from what to cook for dinner to
whether to order the tall or grandé. Given how much consumption is on our minds, the last thing we want to do is
obsess over food more—which is exactly why mindful eating may seem
unappetizing. Plus, who has the time? The strategy has an unfortunate
reputation for involving busywork: incessantly putting down our forks
between bites or sniffing every last morsel.

The latest incarnation of mindful eating inflicts none of that torture.
"Really, it involves eating with intention and attention," explains Michelle May, a physician and the author of the *Eat What You Love, Love
What You Eat* series of books, "so that we eat only when we're hungry,
mostly stop when we're satisfied and truly enjoy food."

To tune in to your hunger cues and become a more mindful eater, try these moves.

1. Start with: Do I really want this?

Taking a brief pause before we have that first bite to ask this simple question helps gauge hunger level and assess why we're eating; perhaps it's more out of boredom or fatigue than a response to an empty stomach. "If you're in a car driving cross-country and you see a gas station, you wouldn't immediately pull off—you'd check your fuel gauge," says May. A simple way to remember to do this: leave a stickie on the computer or laptop that reads "Am I hungry?"

2. Actually sit down

Tactics don't get much easier than this: (1) Place butt on seat. (2) Eat. In a study from the University of Surrey in England published in the *Journal of Health Psychology*, dieters ate granola bars while either watching TV, walking at their own pace for five minutes, or sitting and conversing with a friend. Then they were offered additional snacks. Those who had walked ate more of the bonus munchies than their peers—including five times as much chocolate. Eating on the go may make us overeat later on, reports the study's lead author, Jane Ogden, because we don't notice the amount we've already consumed. So when you do go for fast food, make it more of an experience–as in, have it at a table rather than out of the bag.

3. Act like a baby

Tots find food wondrous: they mush it, pummel it and joyfully smear it all over themselves. As adults, though, we tend to just inhale what's on our plates. But by employing what May calls this "beginner's mind-set" to-

ward eating, we can add enjoyment, which provides more satiety and contentment. All we need to do is notice the aroma and flavor of, say, a pizza slice we're about to shovel down—or just how attractive a dish looks, which is why Instagram-ready foods are our friend. Taking time to plate meals in interesting ways ups the pleasure factor. Susan Albers, a clinical psychologist at the Cleveland Clinic and the author of *Eating Mindfully*, recalls a wedding shower where fruit kebabs were served; she watched guests savor them. "People were eating slowly, really enjoying them," she notes. "How different that would have been if they just had fruit in a bowl."

4. Have lunch anywhere but your desk

Actually eat in the break room. Or better yet, take your lunch outside to a bench in a nearby courtyard or park. "Although you can do multiple tasks when you eat at your desk, your brain can only fully pay attention to one thing at a time," explains May—so you won't fully experience your meal and may end up feeling less than satisfied.

5. Create a food speed bump

Doing a mid-meal assessment of whether we want to keep eating can benefit card-carrying members of the Clean Plate Club. May recommends dividing food on our plates in half—just a quick swipe down the middle with a knife or fork—so that even if we're deep in conversation, we're automatically reminded to check in with our stomach.

6. Go wild with Thai takeout . . .

Or any other ethnic cuisine. "One of my favorite tips is to try more foods from other cultures," says Albers. "Say you're eating a new Indian dish. You're likely to slow down, really pay attention to the flavor and wonder, 'What spices do they use?' It's fun, and it shifts you out of autopilot eating."

7. Don't swear off comfort food

The more you forbid yourself delicious treats, the more likely you are to devour them when your defenses are down (say, after a hard day at the office). "Enjoying a favorite food from childhood, like grilled cheese, can add pleasure and comfort to your day," says May. Too bad these foods often come with a side of guilt. To beat that, she recommends that we reassure ourselves, "I can trust myself to eat in a way that nourishes my body and spirit."

8. Have the candy—just don't keep it handy

Renowned food researcher Brian Wansink, the director of the Food and Brand Lab at Cornell University, is all about setting up our environment so it works *for* us rather than *against* us—and he has an entire book on the topic, *Slim by Design*. In one study he conducted, he found that people consumed 125 fewer calories from Hershey's Kisses at work if they moved the candy dishes from their desks to six feet away from them.

You also get a gut check when you serve food off a counter instead of the table. Wansink discovered that this tweak reduced how much men ate by 28% and how much women ate by close to 10%. Regarding that gender divide, Wansink notes that the men tended to pack away additional helpings while those around them chatted. Needing to get up for their seconds made them less likely to do so.

9. Chew like a cow

No, really, although this is one tactic not to try at a business lunch. Researchers from Brigham Young and Colorado State universities asked one group of people to pay attention to the sounds they made while chewing cookies, pretzels and chips, and another group to eat while wearing headphones. The headphone group ate about 45% more on average than those who could hear their eating. The "crunch effect" suggests that the sound of food is a key sensory cue that helps us regulate how much we consume.

10. Beat buffet syndrome

New research is finding that we can position our bodies to shape the ways we think, act and eat. Called "embodied cognition," the process involves literally firming our muscles to firm our willpower in order to, say, consume unpleasant medication or resist food temptation. So if we're faced with a beckoning spread and considering loading more onto our plates, making a fist or crossing our arms can signal our brains to stop. Of course, this also prevents us from using our hands to serve ourselves more baked ziti.

11. Play with texture

Altering food textures wakes up your taste buds and your sense of food adventure, says Albers. Try freezing grapes, dropping whole-wheat croutons over steamed veggies, placing a slice of creamy avocado between layers of turkey in a sandwich or sprinkling crushed salted pretzels over fro-yo.

12. Follow the rule of two

This one's all about planning your pleasure, courtesy of the Cornell Food and Brand Lab: order a reasonable entrée, plus any two other things you really want, whether that's a glass of pinot and an appetizer or a piece of pie. "People report eating about 25% less, because it doesn't leave them feeling deprived," says Wansink.

13. Clean that cluttered kitchen

True, this tip involves some effort—but it also improves your home decor and possibly your waistline. We're likely to overeat by as much as 34% when our kitchens are a mess of newspapers on the table, unopened mail on the counter and chairs in disarray, finds a recent Wansink study published in *Environment and Behavior*. "Having a neat eating environment helps you feel like the world is less out of control," he explains, "and reduces the chances of eating from anxiety."

14. End the meal on a favorite

Save the best for last, Albers coaches. "We tend to have a poor memory of what we eat, and finishing a meal on a positive note makes us more likely to encode it in our brains," she says. "The more satisfied you are after a meal, the less likely you are to eat a lot later." So if dinner is chicken, salad, mashed potatoes and fruit, but it's really all about the taters, end on those. The food gods never said we couldn't have mashed potatoes for dessert.

Foods You Can't Help But Savor

"We live in a world that stresses instant access and hurrying, and eating is no exception," says psychologist Susan Albers. Truth is, though, eating slowly has a host of benefits, ranging from feeling full for a longer period of time to taking more satisfaction in what we eat. Even for the fast eaters among us, these nine foods have to be consumed slowly by their very nature—and that's a good thing

Wrapped piece of dark chocolate

Go with dark chocolate for the antioxidants— and individually wrapped for the portion control. One study found that when people had to repeatedly unwrap pieces of chocolate instead of diving into one big bar, they downed 30% less.

Mandarin orange

Peeling this fruit and breaking out each sweet segment provides a moment of mindful eating.

Kebabs

These everything-on-a-skewer summer party staples are not only portable but also a feast for the senses, thanks to the marinated meat and brightly colored vegetables.

Whole-wheat spaghetti

Concentration is required to fork and twirl this pasta, making us focus on the food in front of us, not the work project due tomorrow.

Edamame

We have to work at opening each pod, which keeps this healthy side from being a fast food.

Unshelled pistachios

In a study that compared eating unshelled versus shelled pistachios, noshers who had to crack open the nuts consumed 41% less.

Pomegranate

The brilliant red seeds add crunch and visual interest to yogurt, salads and other good-for-you fare.

Artichoke

The ultimate tactile vegetable, a spiky artichoke forces us to appreciate nature's packaging as we peel off one petal at a time and pull it through our teeth.

Crab legs

Eating crab legs takes effort, from cracking them to dipping them in butter. The sound serves as a reminder of how much we're eating (what researchers have dubbed the "crunch effect").

FINDING YOUR FLOW

Losing yourself in something—whether a 5K run or a guitar solo—is a decades-old secret to happiness that is gaining new traction today. The only catch is that you have to be patient

By Mark Remy

EVENTEEN YEARS LATER, I DON'T REMEMBER MUCH ABOUT my best-ever 5K race. It was in Kutztown, Pa. That much I know. I finished in 16 minutes, 29 seconds. Beyond that, things get foggy. Who else was there? What was I wearing? Was it warm or cool? These details are long gone.

I do, however, recall one part in vivid detail.

It was in the third and final mile, over a short downhill stretch. Things were surely painful at that point—I was running faster than ever over that distance—and I had every excuse to slow down. Downhills, after all, are a natural place to catch your breath and let gravity do some of the work.

Instead, I sped up—effortlessly. My turnover increased, with a grace and fluidity that seemed alien. Weightless, swept ahead on my own private jet stream, I sailed past the guy in front of me and on to a personal record.

For those few minutes, time fell away and everything clicked. I was no longer performing a task; I *was* the task.

It was transcendent. Joyous. Surreal. It was, in short, "flow." And it's not quite as mysterious as you might think.

A HAPPY IMMERSION

As defined by Mihaly Csikszentmihalyi, a Hungarian psychologist whose pioneering research in the 1970s introduced the concept, flow is the state of being totally and blissfully immersed in a task, to the exclusion of just about everything else, including one's self. Flow is focus that happens on an almost sublime level, a place where, as Csikszentmihalyi

puts it, "existence is temporarily suspended."

Csikszentmihalyi never set out to study flow, per se. He was researching happiness. While following "chess players, rock climbers, dancers and others who emphasized enjoyment as the main reason for pursuing an activity," he heard many of his subjects describe their own moments of immersive joy as a "spontaneous flow." For these people, it turned out, flow equaled happiness.

Over time, Csikszentmihalyi came to define this state in more precise terms. In "The Concept of Flow," an article he co-authored, he described flow as "a subjective state" with these characteristics:

• Intense and focused concentration on what one is doing in the present moment

• Merging of action and awareness

• Loss of reflective self-consciousness (i.e., loss of awareness of oneself as a social actor)

• A sense that one can control one's actions; that is, a sense that one can in principle deal with the situation because one knows how to respond to whatever happens next

• Distortion of temporal experience (typically, a sense that time has passed faster than normal)

• Experience of the activity as intrinsically rewarding, such that often the end goal is just an excuse for the process

MASTERY IN MOTION

What does this look like from a neuroscientific point of view? Brain scans of jazz musicians, who often enter a flow state when they improvise, offer an answer. In moments of flow, researchers at Johns Hopkins found, activity in the dorsolateral prefrontal cortex slows. That part of the brain is used for planning and self-monitoring—for example, it keeps us from saying the wrong thing at the wrong time. Meanwhile, the medial prefrontal cortex revs up. That's the part we use to express ourselves. In short: during flow, inhibitions fall and creativity rises. Our motions become almost subconscious. And, thanks to the release of neurochemicals such as endorphins, dopamine and serotonin, we feel good.

At its core, flow is about taking on a task that will test your skill level—but not so much so that you'll feel overwhelmed or over-

anxious. Or, as a group of Italian researchers in the 1980s described it, flow is "the balance of challenges and skills when both are above average levels for the individual."

Achieving this balance is critical. In Csikszentmihalyi's view, a mismatch of challenge versus skill can result in anxiety, boredom or just apathy, depending on which way you err. Find the sweet spot between high challenge and high skill, and you'll find flow.

Don't expect to find it easily, though, or often. Flow is an elusive state. "Most estimates are that elites themselves have experienced flow probably 10% of the time in their career," says Colleen Hacker, a professor of kinesiology at Pacific Lutheran University. "It's very rare." (It's telling, Hacker told me, that although I've been running for two decades, I had to reach back 17 years to find my own instance of finding flow. But, in fairness, I've had many experiences while running that I would call, if not flow, then flow-y.)

ORDINARY WONDER

Any of us can experience flow, in a wide range of settings, under the right circumstances. It's not about elite athletes being "in the zone," says Shane Murphy, chair of the department of psychology at Western Connecticut State University. It's about enjoyment. "If you look at Csikszentmihalyi's original research," he says, "people were happiest when they were engaged in activities that challenged them. They experienced flow at work."

Hacker, whose clients are mostly world-class athletes, agrees—with a caveat. "Flow can happen to anybody at any level of any activity," she says, "but you can't will yourself there. It's not performance on demand."

In this way, flow is a lot like love—you can't just wake up one day and decide you'll go find it. All you can do is try to create the conditions that will allow it to happen.

That part, at least, is fairly simple. Try not to dwell on past mistakes or fret over future ones. Find something that you enjoy intrinsically, just for the sake of doing it, something that will challenge you but not too much. Then dive in—and be patient. In other words: don't go looking for flow. Do what you love, and it will find you.

TIME

Editor Nancy Gibbs
Creative Director D.W. Pine
Director of Photography Kira Pollack

MINDFULNESS:
THE NEW SCIENCE OF HEALTH AND HAPPINESS

Editor Lisa Lombardi
Designer Skye Gurney
Photo Editor Patricia Cadley
Writers Jacqueline Andriakos, Dan Bova, Mallika Chopra, Jancee Dunn, Brooke Hauser, Markham Heid, Louisa Kamps, Sharon Liao, Kathleen Mulpeter, Lindsey Murray, Mandy Oaklander, Holly Pevzner, Lissa Rankin, M.D., Mark Remy, Ellen Seidman, Mary Elizabeth Williams
Copy Editor Joseph McCombs
Writer-Reporter Andréa Ford
Editorial Production David Sloan

TIME INC. BOOKS
Publisher Margot Schupf
Associate Publisher Allison Devlin
Vice President, Finance Terri Lombardi
Vice President, Marketing Jeremy Biloon
Executive Director, Marketing Services Carol Pittard
Director, Brand Marketing Jean Kennedy
Finance Director Kevin Harrington
Assistant General Counsel Andrew Goldberg
Assistant Director, Production Susan Chodakiewicz
Senior Manager, Category Marketing Bryan Christian
Brand Manager Katherine Barnet
Associate Prepress Manager Alex Voznesenskiy
Project Manager Hillary Leary

Editorial Director Kostya Kennedy
Creative Director Gary Stewart
Director of Photography Christina Lieberman
Editorial Operations Director Jamie Roth Major
Senior Editor Alyssa Smith
Assistant Art Director Anne-Michelle Gallero
Copy Chief Rina Bander
Assistant Managing Editor Gina Scauzillo
Assistant Editor Courtney Mifsud
Special thanks: Nicole Fisher, Kristina Jutzi, Seniqua Koger, Kate Roncinske

We welcome your comments and suggestions about Time Books. Please write to us at: Time Books, Attention: Book Editors, P.O. Box 62310, Tampa, FL 33662-2310. If you would like to order any of our hardcover Collector's Edition books, please call us at 800-327-6388, Monday through Friday, 7 a.m.–9 p.m. Central Time.

credits

FRONT COVER Peter Hapak/Trunk Archive

BACK COVER (clockwise from top left) Chris Schmidt/Getty Images; G. Victoria/Getty Images; Astronaut Images/Getty Images; Adriana Varela/Getty Images

TITLE PAGE **1** Caracterdesign/Getty Images

CONTENTS **2** Neustockimages/iStock/Getty Images

INTRODUCTION **5** Adelevin/Getty Images

SECTION OPENERS **7, 42, 73** Illustrations by Todd Detwiler

BODY **7** PeopleImages/Getty Images **8** Chris Schmidt/Getty Images **11** Nicole Bengiveno/The New York Times/Redux **12** Peter DaSilva/Polaris **15** Illustrations by Brown Bird Design for TIME **16** Jamie Grill/Getty Images **19** Peopleimages/Getty Images **20** PeopleImages/Getty **21** iStockphoto/Getty Images **23** Illustrations by Heather Jones for TIME **25** Tetra Images/Getty Images **27** Keiji Iwai/Getty Images **29** David Joles/Minneapolis Star Tribune via ZUMA Wire **31** Deborah Jaffe/Getty Images **32** Dave and Les Jacobs/Blend/Getty Images **35** Brand New Images/Getty Images **36** Westend61/Getty Images **39** Henrik Sorensen/Getty Images

LIFE **42** Stigur Karlsson/Getty Images **44** Echo/Getty Images **47** Frank P. Wartenberg/Getty Images **49** Image Source/Getty Images **50** Buddhify **51** (clockwise from top left) Headspace; Insight Timer; Calm; Whil **51** David Joles/Minneapolis Star Tribune via ZUMA Wire **52–53** (from left and top) Lucasfilm Ltd./Twentieth Century Fox Film Corp./Photofest; Gramercy Pictures/Photos 12/Alamy; AMC/Photofest; Columbia Pictures/courtesy Everett Collection; Columbia Pictures/Alamy; Fox Searchlight/Pho-

tofest; NBCUniversal; Walt Disney Pictures **55** Neo Vision/Getty Images **56** Todd Sappington/BloomImages/Getty Images **57** Hero Images/Getty Images **58** Kwaku Alston/Stockland Martel **60** Lisa und Wilfried Bahnmüller/Getty Images **63** Christophe Boisvieux/Corbis Documentary/Getty Images **64** Salvator Barki/Gallo Images/Getty Images **67** Hero Images/Getty Images **69** (clockwise from top left) Laura Cavanaugh/Getty Images; Mark Wilson/Getty Images; courtesy of Mark Zuckerberg via Facebook; Paul Kane/Getty Images **70** Fertnig/Getty Images **71** Courtesy of Brandon Webb/Force 12 Media

SHAPE **73** Jessica Peterson/Getty Images **74** Sporrer/Rupp/Cultura/Getty Images **76** Buddy Bartelsen/Ullstein Bild via Getty Images **77** Klaus Vedfelt/Getty Images **78** Illustrations by Nathalie Dion **79** (clockwise from top left) Lyn Alweis/The Denver Post via Getty Images; no credit; Michael Ochs Archive/Getty Images; Jon Kopaloff/FilmMagic/Getty Images; Otto Greule Jr./Getty Images; B. Christopher/Alamy **80** Jamie Grill/Getty Images **81** Illustrations by Jameson Simpson for TIME **83** Zheka-Boss/Getty Images **84** G. Victoria/Getty Images **87** Jutta Klee/Getty Images **88** (left) Courtesy Kyle Brett; Westend61/Getty Images **89** (top) Gallo Images/Sunday Times/Camera Press/Redux; Chefshots/Eric Futran/Getty Images **90** (top) Envision/Corbis Documentary/Getty Images; JuanMonino/iStock/Getty Images **91** (from left and top) Pindyurin Vasily/Getty Images; Christian Jung/Getty Images; Martin Jacobs/Getty Images; Elizabeth Watt/Getty Images; Kyoshino/Getty Images; Clive Streeter/Getty Images; Valery121283/iStock/Getty Images; Creativeye99/Getty Images; Cynoclub/iStock/Getty Images **93** Izf/iStockphoto/Getty Images **95** Anna Berkut/Alamy

mindful wisdom

"THE WILLINGNESS TO ACCEPT RESPONSIBILITY FOR ONE'S OWN LIFE IS THE SOURCE FROM WHICH SELF-RESPECT SPRINGS."
—JOAN DIDION

"HOW WE SPEND OUR DAYS IS, OF COURSE, HOW WE SPEND OUR LIVES."
—ANNIE DILLARD

"If you can't live longer, live deeper."
— ITALIAN PROVERB

"IF YOU WANT TO BE HAPPY, BE SO."
—ALEKSEY KONSTANTINOVICH TOLSTOY

"Life moves pretty fast. If you don't stop and look around once in a while, you could miss it."
—FERRIS BUELLER

"YOU CAN'T THINK AND HIT AT THE SAME TIME."
—YOGI BERRA

"Nature does not hurry, yet everything is accomplished."
—LAO TZU

"Nothing can bring you peace but yourself."
—RALPH WALDO EMERSON

"WHEN YOU PAY ATTENTION TO BOREDOM, IT GETS UNBELIEVABLY INTERESTING."
—JON KABAT-ZINN

Made in the USA
Middletown, DE
18 January 2020